Orphan Drugs:
A Global Crusade

Abbey S. Meyers

This book was made possible through an unrestricted grant from Medunik Canada whose mission is to improve the health and quality of life of Canadians living with rare diseases.

ISBN 978-0-692-572177

www.abbeysmeyers.com

I have written this book based on my memories and I have made every effort to ensure that the information in this book is accurate.

- Abbey S. Meyers

TABLE OF
CONTENTS

Forward

I am no historian or politician, nevertheless, the story of the Orphan Drug Act begs to be told. I am simply an observer of extraordinary events that unfurled before my eyes, like a flower in bloom. The story involves people with serious health problems who were treated as if their lives were disposable, like a paper plate that is relegated to a garbage bag after the picnic is completed.

My memory of the events in this book is largely accurate, but the sequence or timing of the events may be faulty. This Memoir is simply my effort to document what happened, when and why. The most important factor is nothing ever occurred because of one person's efforts. All advancements occurred because many people put their personal interests aside and worked together with others to reach common goals. That coalition, which became the National Organization for Rare Disorders (NORD), represented unprecedented political strength that could not be ignored.

In 1983, starting with myself, other volunteers and a part time secretary, we built NORD as a national refuge for people with rare disorders and their families. NORD's programs were built not upon things that we thought might help them, but on the services and programs that patients, families and health care workers told us they needed.

Since my retirement, I have experienced health problems that make traveling very difficult so I decided it was time to write this book. I no longer have input into NORD's programs and activities. I do not know if the programs we put in place still exist today. I can only say that I am proud of the non-profit corporation that I left to my successor, and I am astounded at the growth and effectiveness of the orphan disease movement around the world today.

This is a story about the needs of millions of people with rare diseases who were consistently ignored simply because there were not enough of them with each diagnosis. In other words they would not be profitable enough in comparison to treatments aimed at high blood pressure, headaches, arthritis or indigestion, etc. Because corporations did not deem rare diseases to be profitable enough, the unavailability of treatments (nicknamed "orphan drugs" in the medical literature) represented a gaping hole in the health care system. The "Free Market" mindset of business establishments measure potential success according to the rules of "supply and demand"; because rare diseases affect small potential markets, pharmaceutical manufacturers concluded that the "demand" side of the equation was too small to address the "supply".

Nonetheless, there are over 7,000 rare diseases affecting 25 to 30 million Americans and millions more throughout the world! Should they be left to suffer and die without hope simply because they represent minorities that are too small to make businesses rich? The ethical questions became as important as the financial issues.

This is the story of how by working together, ordinary people were able to plug an enormous hole in the health care system when the "free market" did not address their needs. To accomplish this they needed to attract to their cause other patients, physicians, politicians, business leaders, government employees and millions of others throughout the world. They had to learn how the government functions, who the policy makers are, how to influence them, and how to lure disinterested people to their cause.

The passage of federal legislation, the Orphan Drug Act of 1983, was only the first step. This event jump started decades of extraordinary scientific advancements and development of miraculous new treatments for diseases once deemed to be hopeless. But it also kicked off a period of unimaginable price inflation that has put the cost of some orphan drugs beyond the reach of many.

There are many people to thank for their encouragement, their lending of knowledge and talents that went into this book. I started writing it a few years after I retired, and I never stopped tinkering with paragraphs and sentences. First and foremost I have to thank my family for standing by me during all the years that I missed their school plays, music concerts and football games (to name a few). My husband Jerry, and children David, Adam and Laura, got used to my mind being elsewhere even when we sat together at the dinner table or played a game of monopoly on a snowy day. My children are adults with their own families now, and I thank God every day that they are healthy, and they have health insurance which, thanks to ObamaCare, cannot be taken away from them.

I also want to thank my good friends and colleagues who worked with me at NORD for many years: Jean Campbell and Maria Hardin, who were Vice Presidents at NORD, and to this day can still remember the names of people and their contact info long after my Rolodex became passé. Stephanie Putkowski was a nurse who worked tirelessly at NORD administering our research program and talking to distressed patients who needed comfort and hope. And I remain grateful to my former secretary, Audrey Ashley, who for decades saved me from embarrassing exposure as the world's worse speller.

Rob Tomaino deserves my greatest thanks for editing this book and rearranging the presentation of content. Rob is a medical writer who consulted for NORD on various projects, especially the "Rare Disease Database". Without Rob's editing I would have given up on this book long ago. Rob, Steph and several other of NORD's staff worked under Mary Dunkle, NORD's Vice President of Information Services, who translated complicated medical terms into understandable language so people could find out about the disease they or their loved one had, what its causes could be, possible treatments, and if investigational new treatments were being tested how they could find out about clinical trials. NORD's "Rare Disease Database" can be accessed on NORD's website (www.rarediseases.org)

I join with Jean, Maria, Steph and Rob for lunch every few weeks so we can catch up on the things each of us is doing. They represent much of the success NORD had because I always knew they would make the right management decisions. They still remain involved with rare diseases even though they don't work for NORD anymore.

Eric Gervais and his wife, Carole Boyer, have been key to my completing this book and putting it on the Internet so people can read it. They will never know how much their encouragement has meant. Eric is the CEO of Médunik Canada, an orphan drug company that makes American and European orphan drugs available to Canadian patients. Canada has not yet enacted orphan drug legislation despite years of pressure from rare disease support groups in Canada. The parent company of Médunik is Duchesnay, which manufactures Diclegis, a drug to treat nausea during pregnancy. After you read in this book about Eric Gervais and his herculean effort to get Diclegis on the American market, you will understand his great accomplishment for another group of ignored and abandoned patients, pregnant women. Most pharmaceutical companies don't want to test their drugs on women, no less pregnant women, because their perceived risk of liability is too high.

Doris Zallen, Ph.D., also deserves my thanks for helping me in the early days of writing this book. Doris is a Professor at Virginia Tech and she has written several excellent books about genetic testing and bioethical issues. We served together on government advisory committees that were involved with gene therapy protocols. I always felt that judging the science of each research project was equally important to the bioethical issues that were inherent in each experiment, but too often the scientists didn't feel the same way. Doris and I stood together on many of these issues.

There are numerous others who deserve my thanks for helping me to bring this book to completion. Ultimately, anytime I was at wits end, I thought of the staff people who I worked with me at NORD, and was reminded of their devotion to NORD's mission. They knew the work they were doing would touch on many lives, and they stayed with us even though they would have benefitted financially by going into a for-profit corporation.

Even though I cannot name all the people who I owe a great debt to, please know how much I appreciate your advice, encouragement and especially your devotion to the cause of rare "orphan diseases".

Chapter 1

Many Questions, Few Answers

"The future belongs to those who believe in the beauty of
their dreams."

Eleanor Roosevelt

Every parent feels that their child must be perfect. You expect it as
if you have earned normality for your offspring. However, there are
more than 7,000 rare disorders, many of them genetic, and many
parents learn that normality is relative.

Although there is no inherent right for our children to be healthy,
the western industrialized world expects that a child, any sick
child, will be medically treated if the knowledge and treatments
are there. My journey in the orphan disease world began not
because my son was sick, not because he had a rare disorder,
but rather because the medication that eliminated his symptoms
and gave him a chance to live a "normal" life was suddenly
unavailable to him – discontinued by the manufacturer because
it was deemed not profitable enough due to the small potential
number of patients who would buy the medication.

I could accept the years without a diagnosis, the unanswered questions, and the several prior failed treatments, but I could not accept that the only viable, highly effective option for my son was denied to him simply because he had an unusual diagnosis that was not profitable enough. It was an injustice that I could not ignore.

It never occurred to me that finding an effective treatment for my son wasn't the end of our struggles, but only the beginning.

*

David, my eldest son, was born in South Korea in 1968. My husband, Jerry, had been assigned a two year diplomatic mission by the U.S. Army in Pusan, a large South Korean city. Because it was a diplomatic mission, I was able to accompany him.

I still remember lying in a hospital bed in Pusan more than 7,000 miles from my home, my family and just about everything else that I was familiar with. The women who meant the most to me were back in New York, unable to coach me in the art of motherhood. Back in 1968, I could not simply pick up the phone to ask my mother, sister, friends or mother-in-law, "What do I do now?"

Jerry and I had been married two years and David was our first child; we were not experienced in the art of raising a child. As a teenager, I had seen a TV movie about Eskimos on one of those dreary sick days when I stayed home from school. A male and female found each other, they went off on their dog sled to hunt and build their own igloo. The woman's stomach swelled for no apparent reason, then one day a baby was born. The husband examined the child and discovered with alarm that it had no teeth. He told his wife they needed to abandon the child on an ice floe where it would mercifully die. The mother begged and cried until her husband, quite disgusted, allowed her to keep the child so she would at least stop crying. She promised that she would chew the baby's food so he would not starve to death. Eventually the baby grew teeth which satisfied the father. My husband Jerry and I knew as much about babies as those Eskimos.

*

Jerry and I had known each other all of our lives. We were distant relatives and Jerry, his brother and I were good playmates. When we grew older Jerry was always serious and goal oriented. While in college he was attracted to the Reserve Officers' Training Corps (ROTC), and achieved a high enough status to be appointed a Second Lieutenant in the "regular army" when he graduated. That meant he was not in the military "reserve" army which allowed soldiers to serve 2 years on active duty, and the rest of their mandatory time on weekends and summers. Having taken a commission in the "regular" army, Jerry was required to serve at least 3 years on active duty before he could resign.

Jerry initially served 3 years in Germany, and achieved the rank of Captain in the Army. Shortly after he got back to the U.S., he received orders for Vietnam. The war was still ramping up under Lyndon Johnson and later Richard Nixon, so no one in the military could see an end to it. People who made a career in the army expected to go back to Vietnam, Laos and Cambodia over and over again in future years, without their wives and children.

When he came home from Germany at the beginning of 1966 we began a whole different relationship. There was no comparison between him and the men I had been dating,. We became engaged and Jerry decided to resign from the army and try civilian life, but his resignation was rejected. He was told he could not resign until he served a tour of duty in Vietnam. So we prepared for marriage, a short honeymoon, and a one year separation. But we knew when he got home his resignation would be accepted.

A few days before our scheduled wedding in New York in October of 1966, Jerry phoned me from Fort Devens, Massachusetts. He said he was in the hospital and was diagnosed with mononucleosis (also known at the time as "glandular fever"). His temperature was 103 degrees and they would not let him out of the hospital, probably for several weeks. This was devastating news. But when I thought about it I knew he would spend weeks recuperating, and then the army would likely ship him off to Vietnam anyway. And if by some miracle they changed his orders temporarily they still would not let him out of the army until he served that tour in Vietnam.

So with help from my family and friends we switched the wedding from New York to the hospital at Fort Devens. We were married in the hospital chapel. It was indeed a small wedding; the largest guest contingent was Jerry's fellow officers from his unit. Jerry's brother coaxed him out of pajamas and dressed him in a suit for the occasion, but his fever was still high and he could not stand without leaning on something. He was wheeled to the chapel in a wheelchair. Thereafter Jerry joked that he was not responsible for marrying me because he was delirious.

After the ceremony Jerry went back to his hospital bed and I thanked the soldiers for their support and encouragement. I spent my honeymoon evening with my mother-in-law and we flew home on a propeller plane from Boston the next day. That flight was my first one in an airplane, capping the most exciting few days of my life.

*

We were married on October 23, 1966 and Jerry was not allowed out of the hospital because of the mononucleosis until Thanksgiving at the end of November. It was a time of few clear answers so we could not plan for anything.

By the middle of November we wondered if they would really insist on sending him to Vietnam. The doctors had warned, due to the severity of Jerry's infection, that he would have a long slow recovery. Then the answers finally came: because of lingering health questions they would not send Jerry to Vietnam. Instead he could go on a one year "hardship tour" (without me) to the demilitarized zone of South Korea (where there was no active war but always a fear of clashes with the North), OR he could take a 2 year diplomatic assignment (with me) in Pusan. When he told me the choices, there was only one answer. I would go with him and we would have 2 years of a semi-normal life.

Now that I was married and plans were finally definite for the next 2 years of our married life, I had to resign from my job as an assistant art director at a large corporation. I made sure to pack up my art supplies and take them with me to Korea. We sold our cars before we left and bought a used Ford Falcon which, if it needed to be fixed in Korea, was more likely to find parts than Jerry's Volvo or my 1965 Ford Mustang.

I never let Jerry forget that he forced me to part with my bright red 1965 Mustang! In exchange he gave me a metal 1965 red Mustang model that I keep on my desk with its doors and front hood ajar.

*

Although spending two years in South Korea was not the way I imagined I'd begin married life, I was grateful that we had a healthy son born in 1968 at the Baptist Missionary Hospital on Yong Do Island in Pusan. I knew we would return home shortly after his first birthday in 1969. Hopefully, Jerry would be able to leave the army at that time and get a civilian job. I wanted to live in my own culture where I usually understood (even if I disagreed) why people behave the way they do, and what motivates them. Nevertheless, the American culture was undergoing revolutionary changes when we returned home in 1969, and we did not understand the motivations of those who were rioting in the streets and burning their draft cards. Before we returned, Jerry submitted his army resignation again, but the answer came before we packed up our household; the army would not accept his resignation until he served a year in Vietnam. It was a dreadful disappointment, but there was nothing we could do. I would have to live a year in New York with the baby, and without Jerry. Our lives would be on hold again.

Jerry thought it would be more convenient, and less worrisome for him, if I lived with his parents for the year. They had a house in Queens, whereas my mother had a small apartment in Brooklyn with no room for us. So our belongings went into storage and after one month of leave Jerry went off to war in Vietnam.

*

Being away from Jerry was difficult. But I found support without even looking for it. One day I put David in a carriage and went to the army commissary on a local military base. The commissary was a large supermarket for military families. There was a community bulletin board at the commissary, and I noticed an index card reading, "Waiting Wives Club." It was a social group of officers' wives whose husbands were serving in Vietnam.

I knew that I had to join the group so I could relate to women who were in a similar predicament to me; alone raising a small child with a husband off fighting a war at a time when there were riots in major cities against the Vietnam War. Jerry was not for or against the war, but he knew it was his duty to be there. The only other option would be desertion, and that would certainly put a crimp in our plans for a normal life. So I needed friends to commiserate with in the military, to compare single parenting skills, and to push away the ever present fears of not knowing if my husband was coming back injured or even alive.

I learned years later that the Waiting Wives club was modeled as a "support group," much the same as Alcoholics Anonymous or other social networks of people with similar characteristics and concerns. Members of a support group truly give each other support because they know what each person is going through since they have shared similar experiences. At the time I had no idea that support groups would play a major role in the rest of my life.

*

When David was 2 years old Jerry came home from Vietnam. Finally the army allowed him to resign after seven years of active duty. Jerry was an accountant, so it wasn't long before he got a job at Texaco's headquarters in New York City. We moved to an apartment on Long Island. Finally we could live a "normal life."

Around this time, I first noticed that some of David's behaviors were unusual even for a young child. When David started to speak in multi-word phrases he stuttered for several months. Then the stuttering disappeared, but it was replaced with abnormally fast eye blinking. When that stopped he had unusual movements of his head, arms or legs. Some of the movements tended to either disappear or get milder before another involuntary movement appeared. At other times old symptoms persisted and additional movements were added to the old. When I asked why he was doing these things David would say, "I don't know. I can't help it." Often his involuntary movements bothered me more than him because I was looking at him all day. But when the involuntary movements interfered with what he was doing, he would cry in frustration and sometimes from pain because his overworked muscles ached.

After a year in an apartment we bought a house on Long Island and, in May 1971, had another baby, Adam. I asked the pediatrician about David's unusual movements. He called them "tics." Sometimes children get tics for no apparent reason, he said, but they usually disappear. "Don't worry," he said, "He'll outgrow it. Even my son has had an eye blinking tic."

That statement didn't do a thing to ease my concerns.

In nursery school David showed unusual behaviors, particularly an inability to sit still and be quiet. But when he played at the things that interested him the most, particularly building blocks, he couldn't be interrupted. The teacher would announce that it was time to put the blocks away and get into a circle for story time, but David could not stop working with the blocks. Interestingly, when he concentrated on something, his tics would decrease or disappear for a while.

When he started kindergarten these minor problems became more serious, particularly because his teacher was unwilling to tolerate him. She was an older woman who insisted that her pupils obey her commands without question. First it was difficult to get David to focus because he had an attention deficit, but if he focused on something he loved (such as building blocks) he could not be interrupted. His teacher had little patience with boys like David. Simultaneously, his tics worsened, moving from one part of his body to another, and he made involuntary noises ranging from throat clearing to repeatedly sniffing. "Can't you blow your nose?" I would ask. "There's nothing wrong with my nose," he would say, "I just have to make that noise. I don't know why."

I would ask the pediatrician what to do. He didn't know what was wrong. David's facial tics made him look different to children of his own age, so they avoided him. His mouth would twitch and he would shake his head uncontrollably, as if trying to shake off hair hanging down on his eyes. David's arms swung around violently before any purposeful movement of his arms, until in second grade he could hardly feed himself. His arms would flail before he picked up his fork, he would get food on his fork, then his arms would swing out violently and the food would land on the wall half-way across the room. Jerry and I would argue about it. "He can't help it," I would say, but Jerry would insist it was just a behavioral problem. "He can stop it if he wants to," he would insist. But no one had any answers—not the teachers, not the doctors, and least of all me. My heart broke for my child without control over his body.

*

The very worst time was in 1976 when David was about 8 years old. Besides his flailing arms, his legs began incomprehensively moving in ways he tried to subdue. He would compulsively stamp on the floor and then he would tell me how tired he was because his arms and legs would not stop moving. So at home he tried sitting on his legs, tucking them under himself to stop the movements. But his legs would not stop, and instead his whole body, sitting Indian-style on the floor, was jumping several inches off the floor. I wondered if I was hallucinating when I watched this, because the strength needed to lift his whole body, sitting Indian style, off the floor seemed like more strength than a child would be capable of.

One Sunday morning I was watching David as he tried to read the comic section of the newspaper on the floor, while his body jumped compulsively. He could not steady his head enough to read. I was ready to cry. Instead of washing the breakfast dishes and cleaning up I decided to sit down and read the Sunday newspaper. I picked Parade magazine from the stack of newspapers and began to read.

It was a story about a teenager named Orrin Palmer. He had a strange neurological disease named Tourette syndrome (TS). The disorder was named after a French doctor, Georges Gilles de la Tourette, who studied movement disorders under France's famous research neurologist, Dr. Jean-Martin Charcot. TS is characterized by involuntary repetitive tic-like movements and noises.

I sat in my chair mesmerized. I could not believe what I was reading. I read descriptions of some of the tic-like movements: rapid eye blinking, facial grimaces, head shaking, foot stamping; then the noises: throat clearing, nose sniffing, and sometimes words involuntarily repeated over and over.

"Jerry," I screamed. "Come here, I found out what's wrong."

Jerry rushed into the room and picked up the article. He started reading. "This is beyond belief," he said. "Whoever heard of a diagnosis made possible by a Sunday magazine?" But he agreed; the article listed David's symptoms. What to do now?

*

On Monday morning, I stuffed the article into my purse and drove to the pediatrician's office. I had no appointment and I thought the nurse would give me a hard time. But I told her that for years the doctor has known something was wrong with my son but he couldn't diagnose it. I read an article yesterday that lists all of his symptoms, and I needed to see the doctor right away. She checked with the doctor and he saw me. I gave him the article and he read it.

"I think you're right," he said. "But I need to find out where to refer you." He made a few calls to his colleagues and a few hours later he told me that luckily the Tourette syndrome world guru was Dr. Arthur Shapiro at Mount Sinai Hospital in New York City. "Let me know what he says," said the pediatrician as he handed me Dr. Shapiro's phone number.

I phoned Dr. Shapiro's office for an appointment. If we wanted to see him at Mt. Sinai the appointment would be several months away, but if we wanted to see him at his private office in Westchester we could see him in 3 or 4 weeks. I made the appointment there.

*

Dr. Shapiro diagnosed David with TS and carefully explained the disease and its treatment. He explained that it was a neurological movement disorder, not a psychiatric illness; it was first described in a medical paper by Georges Gilles de la Tourette published in 1884. Often the movements and noises are accompanied by compulsive behaviors. Because the symptoms are so bizarre, people with severe TS have been historically treated as mental patients, primarily because of the unusual symptoms and because no one knew what caused the odd behaviors. Some people with milder symptoms have been able to live a normal life if they find ways to cope with it. For example, people with TS can often substitute one symptom for another, so instead of making loud noises in public they may be able to substitute low noises until they get to a place where they can safely let out a loud sound. Therefore, a person with head shaking can grow long hair, so they look like they are shaking hair away from their face. That makes a tic understandable to onlookers, and it is accepted as a normal but "nervous" behavior. It is not nervous at all, but anxiety can make the symptoms worse.

In fact, just about everyone knows someone who has what they consider a "nervous tic." But it is not TS unless it includes both motor tics and involuntary sounds or words. In the worst cases the words can include swear words which is medically called "coprolalia." But that phenomenon is extremely rare, and it is very crippling when it occurs. Interestingly, coprolalia can also occur in stroke victims whose facility for speaking has become impaired. They may not be able to communicate through words or sentences, but their ability to automatically use curse words to express anger or frustration can remain unimpaired.

Dr. Shapiro made it clear that there was one medication he could give David, but it could have a powerful sedative side effect. Some people chose not to take medicine, and they live as best they can with the symptoms. Sometimes, just knowing what you have, and being able to explain it to others, is enough to ease their fears. Others feel at all costs they want the symptoms to disappear.

I brought home written information about TS to give to David's teachers, and I joined the Tourette Syndrome Association (TSA). I gave TS pamphlets to the teachers but it didn't help very much, mostly because the main classroom requirement for all children continued to be, "Sit still and be quiet." At that time there were no provisions for children with handicaps, and even though education was compulsory, the school had the right to refuse services to children who were not like other children. Many children with cerebral palsy, mental impairments, autism, etc., were refused free public education in American schools until several years later when Congress passed the "Education for All Handicapped Children Act".

But it did help David to know there was a reason for his body to be out of control. He told us, "I kept telling you I couldn't help it. Why didn't you believe me?"

Nothing in life has reinforced our guilt more than those words.

*

Dr. Shapiro was right, the only medicine approved by the Food and Drug Administration (FDA) to treat Tourette syndrome was Haldol (haloperidol), a major tranquilizer. We tried it, and it did indeed calm his symptoms, but it also put him to sleep in the classroom and made him gain weight rapidly. The idea was to titrate the dose to use the least amount of medicine while calming the involuntary movements. Years later I had to laugh when at a medical meeting about Tourette syndrome a doctor made a statement that "Haldol always works." An audience member stood up and said, "Sure it always works. It will even stop an elephant from stampeding by making a zombie out of him."

After months of experimenting, I asked the doctor if there were any other drugs we could try. He named some others that ranged from antidepressants to seizure medicines. None of them were approved by the FDA as a treatment for TS because no pharmaceutical company was interested in doing studies necessary for FDA review. But it became so obvious that we needed to get David off Haldol, we tried the other drugs, one by one singly or in combination.

When we returned every few months to see Dr. Shapiro we would report that the new medicines weren't working very much better than the drugs we had already tried. It was a matter of which side effects were easier to cope with. I worried that David was losing his childhood to drug side effects. David was around 10 at this point and no progress in treating him had been made.

Finally, Dr. Shapiro said that there was a medicine sold in Europe that he was trying on two or three other TS patients and it seemed to have fewer sedating side effects. But the drug, with the generic name "pimozide," was not approved for sale in the United States. It was being tested in people with a more common disease than

TS, and if it worked on that disease it would eventually become commercially available. If we wanted to try it on David, he would have to participate in a "clinical trial," and we would have to follow all the rules required by the FDA.

We agreed, and Dr. Shapiro gave us enough pills for the first 3 months. We would have to return every 3 months afterward to pick up another 3 months' supply of pimozide. Additionally, David would need laboratory blood tests every month to make sure there were no unforeseen safety problems with the drug. And both David and I (as his parent) would have to sign an "Informed Consent" document which would explain the reason for the experiment, the possible risks and benefits that could arise from taking the drug.

The drug was being tested by McNeil Laboratories, a division of the corporate giant, Johnson & Johnson; a company with the strong consumer image of caring for babies and children.

*

We lived up to most of the rules, and returned every 3 months for the next supply of pills. But with a young growing family, when our insurance company refused to pay for David's monthly blood tests, I decided to get the tests every 6 to 8 weeks instead of every 4 weeks. We simply could not afford to pay for monthly blood tests, but the insurance company said they would not pay for anything in relation to an experimental drug. Usually, all medical costs for people in clinical trials are paid by the drug company, but the company didn't care whether pimozide was ever approved for a disease as rare as Tourette syndrome (at the time TS prevalence was estimated to be 100,000 cases in the United States, but there were not even 10,000 Americans diagnosed with TS at that time).

I learned many years later that Dr. Shapiro's records of his pimozide patients were eventually audited by the FDA, and he got into trouble for not making sure that David had taken the mandatory monthly blood tests. I explained to his wife, Dr. Elaine Shapiro, that I had reduced the frequency because we could not afford the monthly expense. She understood, but the fact remained that no doctor ever wants his wrist slapped by the FDA, and Dr. Shapiro did not deserve the reprimand.

*

Somewhere very late in 1975, I found out that I was pregnant again. I had a newfangled birth control contraption called an IUD (intrauterine device) put in my uterus, and it fell out. I had a dream that I gave birth to a daughter, and when I woke up I was profoundly disappointed that it was only a dream. I prepared myself for having a third boy.

On one of our visits to Dr. Shapiro I explained that I was pregnant, and we wanted to know if TS was hereditary. He said that in his original journal article, Gilles de la Tourette had suggested that TS is most likely inherited. "But I've never seen any evidence of a genetic component," said Dr. Shapiro. We had never known anyone in our families who had any similar symptoms of TS, so I assumed Dr. Shapiro was correct.

That put me at ease because before Jerry and I married we went to see our family physician (most members of our extended family in Brooklyn used the same doctor), and asked if he knew of any hereditary diseases in our family that might change our mind about having children. He said no, there were no genetic diseases in the family except he could guarantee us that our children would have high blood pressure (a family problem).

*

When David was taking pimozide he did very well. His symptoms were hardly noticeable, and he was not falling asleep at school. He was 10 years old and I was greatly relieved that we had finally found a treatment that was effective and had fewer side effects. But a year later, when we visited Dr. Shapiro to get the next supply of the drug, he handed me the medicine vial and said, "Unfortunately, this is the last pimozide I can give you."

He explained that the clinical trial of pimozide for the prevalent disease was finished, and the drug was ineffective on that disease, so the company decided not to develop the drug for the American market.

"But what about the people with Tourette syndrome who have responded to pimozide?" I asked in disbelief.

His answer was simple. "For Tourette syndrome, pimozide is an orphan drug."

I had never heard the phrase "orphan drug" before, but the term would become central to my life for many, many years. An orphan drug is a treatment for a rare disease. Pharmaceutical companies have historically made their decisions on which drugs to develop based on the size of the potential market for each drug. For example, medications for hypertension, indigestion, high cholesterol, arthritis, etc., were developed because the markets comprised millions of people, and therefore the drugs would be very profitable.

These drugs also appealed to investors for the same reasons. In the early 1980s, the investment community generally believed that a "blockbuster" drug was a pharmaceutical that brought in $100 million in annual sales. Today, a "blockbuster" drug is a medicine that sells $1 billion or more in a year, and several orphan drugs are in this category not because their market is big, but simply because of their high prices.

But during the time my son was treated with pimozide, orphan drugs did not have that potential. If the market for a TS medication could only be sold to a maximum of 100,000 people in the United States, companies believed it would be unlikely that the sales of the drug would exceed the costs of developing it. So the pharmaceutical industry simply ignored orphan drugs. Even when an academic scientist had already discovered a treatment for a rare disease, no pharmaceutical company would manufacture it.

At the time, I was not yet versed in the problem of orphan drugs. Staring at Dr. Shapiro in amazement, I could only say, "You're kidding."

"No," he replied. "There are many things to kid about, but not orphan drugs."

I was stunned. But before I had even left Dr. Shapiro's office, I'd already vowed to do something to reverse this travesty – to face down this injustice and find a solution not only for Tourette syndrome, but for all rare diseases.

The only question was – where do I start?

Chapter 2

Quest for treatment

"Start by doing what is necessary, then do what is possible, and suddenly you are doing the impossible."

St. Francis of Assisi

My son was a commodity. All children are a commodity in a health environment dictated by maximizing profit over all else. Although the rational part of my brain understood this, the emotional part of my brain did not.

I was frustrated and disappointed, but deep down I was not surprised. This was not my first experience of children being treated as commodities. It had occurred on the other side of the planet in South Korea.

During my time in Pusan, I had befriended an officer's wife, Ilsa, who was a Dutch national. She had been a nurse and her husband was a doctor. When she mentioned to some of her Dutch friends, who worked for the government of the Netherlands, that she was going to accompany her husband to Korea, they asked her if she would visit some orphanages and find out whether Dutch families could adopt the orphans. On one of her trips to visit these orphanages she asked me to accompany her. I went with her, and I was very moved by the children I saw. Some of the babies in cribs had oddly shaped heads, probably because they were not taken out of their cribs enough. Instead they lay on their back in their cribs most of the time, day after day, and the back of their heads became flat instead of round.

Most of the orphans were females, because they were not valued as much as boys. Male children could share the workload with their fathers. But many of the orphans, boys and girls, were there because they were not pure Korean; their fathers were American GIs. These children faced a lifetime of intense discrimination because they did not look like other Koreans, and they had no Korean ancestry to refer to. In fact, American GIs seemed to leave babies in many of the countries that our military has occupied, and soldiers took little responsibility for the mayhem they left behind, particularly in Asia. When my friend Ilsa asked the manager of the orphanage if she was interested in allowing adoptions to families in the Netherlands, the manager asked "how many children?" Ilsa said that she could take quite a lot… even all of the children in the orphanage. This alarmed the orphanage manager. She said, "All of them? This is my business! If you take all of them, I will have no business."

I have never forgotten that day, those children, or the orphanage manager who cared more for her flourishing business than the human beings in her care. The children were commodities—assets that just happened to be human. I tried to comprehend the benefit of being born a male simply because they could share heavy work, and because it was a son's duty to take care of their parents in their old age. A girl was just another mouth to feed. Apparently, the orphanage manager found no ethical duty to ensure her wards could join a family and enjoy the love and security of caring parents.

I learned so much during those 2 years about prejudice, kindness and cultural gaps that are the deepest abyss of human relationships. Because of my mother's experience of earning lower wages than men, I began to see that many nations around the world have undervalued women in different ways. Since women comprise approximately 50% of the population in all societies, religions, businesses and governments tend to use only half of their society's labor and brainpower. What a waste!

I knew gender inequality was a big problem in the United States, but I had hoped my country was better than relegating children, especially children that needed medical help, to commodities.

I was wrong.

*

My first priority after that fateful meeting with Dr. Shapiro was to figure out what to do about treatment for David now that we could no longer get pimozide. My second priority was to delve into the orphan drug issue, find out what to do about it, and fix it.

It wasn't easy because I was faced with new problems and a growing family. It was August of 1976 that our daughter Laura was born. My dream had come true. When I awoke in the hospital I asked the nurse, "What did I have?" She answered, "You had a girl", I said, "You must have made a mistake. I only have boys". I slept again and when I woke up I told the nurse: "I had a dream that I had a girl". "You did" she said. Only then did I believe her!

When Laura was 4 months old, we moved to Connecticut. Jerry's office was moved from Manhattan to Westchester, and his company offered financial incentives to move employees closer to the office. Instead of buying a house in a Connecticut housing development, we chose a house on a hill in a small town just north of Danbury. I loved the house, the children and the dog, but as soon as snow fell I could not get out of the garage until everything defrosted (sometime in the spring). The only things that moved outside our picturesque window during winter were squirrels and deer. I felt as if I had moved to Stepford, Connecticut!

Rather than looking at squirrels all day I contacted the Tourette Syndrome Association (TSA) to offer starting a Connecticut chapter. When the people at the TSA found out I was willing to volunteer, they immediately asked me to join their Board of Directors. It met once per month in Manhattan, and Jerry bought a snow blower so I could get my car down the hill to attend meetings.

When I went to the first board meeting I learned that the TSA was only about 2 or 3 years old. One family with a child who had TS had put an ad in a newspaper asking any family with TS to contact them. They were contacted by several families that also lived in New York City, so they had to ask, "How rare can this disease be?" Because Dr. Shapiro was located in New York, he tended to diagnose many who were New York residents, and he advised his patients to join the TSA. Membership was growing as news about TS would reach far beyond New York, and the TSA eventually became a truly national organization.

At the Board meeting they put a piece of paper in front of me and asked which job I wanted to do. They were obviously desperate for help. I looked at the list and knew I didn't want to fundraise, I knew nothing about medicine so I didn't want to be a medical liaison, I rejected several other choices until I got to "Legislative Affairs." I chose that issue because of the new federal law that required school districts to provide public education to children with disabilities: "The Education for All Handicapped Children Act". I needed to know what the law said, how it would affect my son, and how it would help all children with TS and other handicapping conditions. I didn't look at any squirrels after that day because I had no free time.

*

Once the last supply of pimozide was used up in 1979, David had several months without medicine. His symptoms were very disruptive. So I contacted Dr. Donald Cohen at Yale University. Dr. Cohen was a world renowned expert on autism and Tourette syndrome. I told him about pimozide and asked if he knew of any alternatives. He told me he was starting a clinical trial on another drug. So far they had just done animal studies which indicated the medicine did reach the brain synapses that they expected it to (in mice), but there was no indication yet that it would work in humans. The good part was it was not a psychiatric drug; it was a high blood pressure drug that had been on the market for several years. It had a good safety profile in blood pressure patients.

When David was 11 years old, he was the second person with Tourette syndrome to go on clonidine (Catapres) at the Yale Child Study Center in New Haven, CT. He had to spend several days in Yale New Haven hospital, and I was there when they first administered it to him through intravenous. He was not sedated, he spoke with the doctor, and before they stopped the IV the doctor asked him to sign something. David's hand went out to grab the pen and there was no repetitive motion that always made it so hard for him to put a fork in his mouth or to write with a pencil. That day he spoke and moved like he was a normal healthy boy. Later they administered clonidine by pill, and David has been taking it for over 30 years now. He knows he has TS, he feels he has TS when he misses a dose of his medicine, but has no noticeable symptoms.

Clonidine does not work on everyone with TS, but thankfully it worked on him. I am beyond grateful that we found an effective treatment for David, but it was a treatment – not a cure. Nothing will ever cure him. The goal was to reduce the symptoms that interfered with the functions of his daily life. Nothing ever erased all of the symptoms, but they were reduced to manageable levels so he could live a productive and fulfilling life.

When our daughter Laura was born David was 8 years old and Adam was 5. By the time Laura was old enough for kindergarten it was obvious that she had TS. I explained it to her and to her teachers, and she was able to get through her early school years without medicine. When she finally needed medicine she went on clonidine immediately, so she never had all the side effects that David had suffered from other drugs.

Since doctors at Yale were treating David, and later Laura, our family became part of genetic studies on Tourette syndrome. They asked about evaluating Adam so I allowed them to. They felt that Adam also had TS but I disagreed with that diagnosis since he had no motor or vocal tics that lasted more than a year (required under TS diagnostic criteria at the time). He did have attention deficit disorder (ADD), but he learned how to manage it by insisting on no distractions in his working/studying environment. But he never had the involuntary motor and vocal tics that were the basis for a TS diagnosis.

Nevertheless, I often remember my conversation about genetics with Dr. Shapiro. For the record, Dr. Gilles de la Tourette was right and Dr. Shapiro was wrong; TS is genetic. Many of the thought leaders in the field believe that tic disorders are a long continuum of one disease, ranging from "Passing Tics of Childhood" (which goes away in a few months) to the severest form, Tourette syndrome.

Thus in the families of people who have Tourette syndrome, you can often find relatives who have mild tics that do not disrupt their lives. Instead they are pegged as "nervous" simply because society wrongly believes that tics are nervous habits.

*

The most important thing I've learned in my work with disease charities over the years is that most people get involved because of a family member or friend, but you cannot solve the problems of your loved one without solving the problems of other people's loved ones. I could not solve the Orphan Drug problem for my son. It had to be solved for all the people with all rare diseases who needed treatment but could not get it.

Yes, David got help through the Education for All Handicapped Children Act, but many other children with TS were helped by everything I learned and all the newsletter articles and pamphlets I wrote to help parents understand their child's rights. TS symptoms were so unusual, we didn't have all the answers, but we surely did try. I remember thinking which other diseases cause noises in the classroom, and how should we advise teachers to handle it?

In the days before the Internet it was very difficult to do literature research, so I asked a doctor friend to get any journal articles from his hospital librarian about children whose health problem included noises. He came back with two or three articles about children with cystic fibrosis (CF) whose coughing in the classroom interferes with the hearing of other children. I found through those articles that no teacher would dare to ask a child with CF to leave the classroom because of their coughing, and if you ignore it everyone in the classroom will eventually forget how annoying it is. That was a good common sense solution, except it doesn't work when a child has coprolalia and yells out curse words in the classroom! Defining a problem is the easy part, finding a solution is the hard part.

As much as I bugged the teachers and complained to principals, in some grades David got tremendous help, while in other grades he got none. When his hands were flying all over the place he could not write, so another student was assigned the job of writing notes using carbon paper, and giving David the copy. David's mind was brilliant, and he could do math problems in his head. On tests he could write the answers to math problems which were largely correct, but he would fail the test because his math teacher wanted him to write out the entire example to show how he figured it out.

When he got to higher grade levels we sued the school district. But we lost the case (and $5,000 in legal fees) because the school insisted that they were educating him sufficiently. It is very difficult for parents to prove otherwise. After that lawsuit when I complained everybody in the school listened because they did not want another legal case, but David learned to hate school. To him sitting still and being quiet was a punishment and he never got over it.

When he graduated from high school I registered David in a community college in Maine to study Building Construction Technology. He wanted to be a builder and would not even consider any other option. Then in August, just before we were going to take him to Maine, he refused to go. "I hate school" he said, "If I have to sit in a classroom one more day in my life I think I'll die" . So David went to work in the building trades and just like in nursery school, even to this day, he is only happy when he is building something beautiful or tearing it apart to see how it works.

We insisted that he had to get health insurance if he was not in school, because if he was not in college, he was not allowed to continue coverage under our family health insurance policy. David's employer did not offer insurance, so I called nine or 10 insurance companies to get a statement of their health insurance benefits, and the cost. But NONE of the companies agreed to give him a policy at any price because he had a "pre-existing condition". I explained that TS is not an expensive disease, and his only related cost was $8 per month for a generic blood pressure drug. But they would not sell him a policy. I said OK, why don't you give him a policy to cover a broken leg or pneumonia, everything except the costs related to Tourette syndrome? The answer from all of the companies was "No, we do not give health insurance to people with any pre-existing condition".

Angrily I answered, "You mean you don't give health insurance to the people who really need it? You only sell it to healthy people?" And that horrible predicament has persisted for millions of Americans until "The Affordable Care Act" (ObamaCare) became federal law.

*

I can remember back to the support group meetings we had at TSA meetings. Parents were always complaining about their TS children who had unbelievable energy. One parent complained that her son refused to go to college, so she was trying to figure out what trade would make him happy. Among the odd jobs that he picked up, he worked for a moving van company, and he liked that job because he came home tired every night. His hyperactivity was a major problem in his life and he rarely got tired from any physical activity, but moving furniture was satisfying for him and enabled him to sleep at night. So the parents, who were college educated middle class parents, bought their son a moving van company.

While other parents with healthy children would worry if their child's SAT scores would be high enough to get them into a good college, I worried about simply getting David through high school. I had little in common with other middle class parents in our neighborhood because they did not have children with handicaps. I identified with parents whose children had TS because we had the same hopes and dreams for our children, but we could only face reality together.

It was heartwarming to speak to parents whose children did not let TS ruin their lives. The young man who was subject of the *Parade Magazine* article, Orrin Palmer, went on to become a physician even though he had very severe TS symptoms. Some people with TS were able to graduate from college and become professionals, while others gave up early and hardly left their homes. What differences in motivation did they have? Where could I find the coping mechanisms that would help patients and their families to live productive lives?

I could never get David to love learning. He just wanted to move around without restraints, to work so hard all day that he would be tired every night, and never be constrained by a desk, an office or a room where he had to sit still and be quiet. Nevertheless, we could not help but regret that David did not want to go to college because his life in the building trades would be a hard one. History shows whenever the economy falters, as it does periodically, slowing construction is the first sign of a pending recession. Nevertheless, David's life has been a success to him and his family. He has a successful marriage and three beautiful daughters, and he builds beautiful things, which has always been his ultimate goal.

Eventually, our second son, Adam, did go to the community college in Maine that had courses in building construction technology. When he graduated he became an electrician.

*

In 1979 I wrote a grant application for the TSA which was submitted to the New York State Department of Mental Retardation and

Developmental Disabilities (OMRDD). TS is a developmental disability because it starts in childhood and lasts throughout life. We knew if we could intervene and get TS children diagnosed early, they would be more likely to escape the many problems that undiagnosed people often suffered. And they needed mental health services as they were growing up in order to grasp coping skills that they would need for the rest of their lives.

I knew, for example, that when our daughter first exhibited TS symptoms she would not be viewed as bizarre or behaviorally abnormal because she could explain to people (including her classmates) that she had a neurological movement disorder. This is why we were able to avoid giving her medicine until she grew much older. Every once in a while, when her teacher would be absent, a substitute teacher would tell her to stop moving around or stop making noise, and she explained why she couldn't obey their wishes. One substitute teacher could not accept her explanation so Laura said, "I'm going to the nurse's office, and she'll come here to explain it to you." And she did exactly that!

Laura also learned what her best learning style was; she found that she learned best if she could read a book while hearing the recorded book on tape at the same time. She was enrolled in the Library for the Blind, and every new school term she would find out what text books she needed recorded on tape. So she would listen to the book while reading it, and ultimately got her Bachelor's Degree and Master's Degree in Social Work.

So the TSA grant application to New York State was aimed at early diagnosis and intervention for children with TS. That was the first grant application that I wrote and submitted anywhere, and to everyone's surprise it was funded!

At the time, the TSA had only one or two administrative employees in a donated office in Bayside, New York. The grant meant that we would have to move and rent an office, and we needed to hire someone to do the work outlined in the grant. These things represented major changes, and some people don't take change very well. At one point, one of the Board members suggested maybe we should not accept the grant. Thankfully, logical people prevailed, they hired a social worker, and they moved the TSA to a store-front where they had room for more employees.

It was my job to supervise the social worker because I knew what the grant proposal promised to do. After one month, however, the social worker called me to say that she would be leaving the TSA because she just heard that she got a teaching job at a local university. The TSA grant was only for one year, and there was 11 months left on the contract, so I was not happy to hear this news. When I told the Board of Directors what happened they asked me if I could possibly do the job for the remaining contract. This would mean I would have to resign from my volunteer Board position, give up the Connecticut chapter responsibilities, and commute from Connecticut to Queens, New York every day. I agreed without realizing that the one year commitment would turn out to be 5 years.

*

Laura was only 4 years old when I started working. It was 1980, and since many other charities for rare diseases were based in New York, I called them to ask if they were affected by the "orphan drug" problem. Some didn't know what I was talking about because they were so far away from finding any treatment that it never occurred to them that drug companies would refuse to make a treatment commercially available to them. Others said yes, they already had experienced the problem; academic scientists had discovered a treatment, but no drug company was willing to manufacture it and jump through all the hoops that the FDA would require of them. Few of them realized that the FDA was a consumer protection agency, which was created to protect us from unsafe or ineffective treatments.

One person I spoke to at that time was Marjorie Guthrie, the widow of folk singer Woody Guthrie and mother of Arlo Guthrie. Woody had died of Huntington's disease, and as soon as Marjorie comprehended the devastation that HD would bring to families, she dedicated the rest of her life to finding the gene that caused it, encouraging the search for a treatment, and ultimately a cure.

Marjorie used to be a professional dancer with Martha Graham's Dance Company. Woody Guthrie was a famous folk singer who wrote so many famous American songs that he was a legend in his own time (e.g., "This Land is Your Land," "This Train is Bound for Glory," "Hard Traveling" and many more). When she was a young dancer someone came up with an idea to have Woody Guthrie sing his songs to a live audience while the Martha Graham company would dance on stage to his music.

The way Marjorie told it, rehearsals were a disaster primarily because Woody never sang any of his songs the same way. But the dancers could not change their steps to accommodate new versions of his songs. They noticed that Woody seemed to like talking to Marjorie, so they assigned her the task of explaining that he needed to keep his songs the same for all of their rehearsals and performances.

It was not long after that they were married, and they settled into an apartment in Brooklyn, my home town. I grew up in Brooklyn, and no one ever mentioned that the famous country boy, Woody Guthrie, was living there. But much of what Woody and Marjorie lived through was tragic, including the loss of a 4 year old daughter in a fire.

Woody had a habit of going off and disappearing for a few days or weeks at a time. Marjorie knew that he had unexplainable urges to ride the trains like a hobo, and she would get the word out to friends that Woody was missing again, and if he turned up at their door, please send him home. Marjorie worried that she needed to find a way to bring in her own income so she could raise two sons and a daughter. Woody had been married before, so she could not count on consistency of his ability to make a living, or of staying in their marriage.

Thus, Marjorie bought a house in Howard Beach, Brooklyn and opened a dance school for children. Woody's odd behavior and involuntary movements became incomprehensible, and people often interpreted his behavior as drunkenness. Eventually he was diagnosed with Huntington's disease. A doctor explained HD to Marjorie and she cried for three days. Unlike TS, Huntington's disease is a terminal illness.

HD is genetic, and if you have a parent with the disease you have a 50% chance of inheriting the disease, which meant that Marjorie's three children were at risk. The symptoms do not usually appear until a person reaches their 40's, 50's or 60's. That means it occurs largely after a person has had their own children, with a 50% chance of passing the disease on to them. Woody's mother had HD. Marjorie told me that one day when he returned from school Woody found his mother with her head in the oven of their gas range, trying to kill herself. Apparently, she knew the deterioration that she faced.

The symptoms of Huntington's disease start with involuntary movements that become so severe over time that a person cannot take care themselves. Then their mind deteriorates. They have a hard time eating sufficiently, and their body uses so many calories from constant movements that a person in advanced stages of HD can literally starve to death. It is a disease of body and mind, a tragedy that takes 10 to 15 years to kill a person.

Marjorie could not pay to keep Woody in a private hospital. So he was admitted to Kings County mental hospital, owned by New York City. Then she divorced him in order to not be financially responsible for the cost of his care.

As a child and teenager, I used to walk by that hospital because it was close to my home. It was a mysterious grassy area with many shade trees, surrounded by a high metal fence. I never saw a person walking on the groundsm but it made me wonder who was housed there and why. I never imagined that I would one day know the wife of a legendary musician who resided at that hospital for more than a decade, and that woman did exactly what my mother did for her daughters; she put the children's welfare first. Marjorie needed to raise her children no matter how strained her resources would become, and no matter what amount of criticism she received over the divorce.

As a teenager, when I got together with friends we would sing folk music because someone always brought a guitar, and I never knew we were singing Woody Guthrie's salute to America, while he was dying a few blocks away from my home.

*

After three days, Marjorie stopped crying, and in 1967 she put together a charity titled, "Committee to Combat Huntington's Disease" (today it is the Huntington's Disease Society of America). She used her contacts in the press to get publicity, and she twisted arms of famous people to help raise money.

After surveying the field of disease charities, and learning as much as she could about medical research, she realized that she could never raise enough to finance Huntington's disease research because it is outrageously expensive. Marjorie decided that the government needed to target research on HD, the way they target research on cancer. It was not initially apparent to her that all politicians fear getting cancer, but they don't fear contracting Huntington's disease.

Nevertheless Marjorie accomplished enough in her lifetime to eventually have government funded scientists find the HD gene.

Huntington's disease is a nightmare, and although there is a better treatment now to make symptoms a little more tolerable, there is still no treatment to slow or stop the relentless progression of the disease. However, today it is possible to take a genetic test to learn if you have the HD gene, and it is also possible through in vitro fertilization to have a child that does not have the HD gene. Nevertheless, most people with HD in their family chose not to take the genetic test. They face the same dilemma as people with Alzheimer's in their family; why look into the crystal ball if there is no treatment available? They would rather not know what their fate is.

I met Marjorie in the late 1970s when I was volunteering at the Tourette Syndrome Association. While Marjorie concentrated on getting government funding for research on Huntington's disease, others in her organization felt that research money should also come from charities that raise money for biomedical research. So a nonprofit splinter group organized with its sole focus on raising research funds. The President of that group was Ruby Horansky, whose husband died of HD.

Before Ruby started another charity for Huntington's disease, she served on the Board of Directors of the Committee to Combat HD.

she met a man whose wife died of HD, at the Board meetings of the Committee. Each of them had three children, all at risk of getting HD. They married and the last time I talked to Ruby two of her three children had HD, and I don't know how many of her second husband's children became affected.

Because Marjorie and Ruby were entirely devoted to Huntington's disease, even though they disagreed on the fastest way to find the cure, the two rivals were cordial to each other and both supported creation of a coalition for rare disease support groups focused on solving the orphan drug dilemma.

*

Marjorie told me she would help to find a solution to the orphan drug problem and she vowed to teach me how to lobby. Her help and advice during those years was a blessing that I will never forget. The most important thing that Marjorie taught me was to be humble. She took me to Washington for a meeting with the new young FDA Commissioner, Dr. Donald Kennedy. Years later Dr. Kennedy became the editor of the prestigious journal Science. But at the time he was talking to leaders of disease organizations, trying to get their support for proposed changes he wanted for the FDA. He talked in the alphabet soup of Washington DC, mentioning NDA's, PLA's, etc. I felt like a teenager walking accidently into a class of advanced physics.

"Excuse me," Marjorie raised her hand, "I'm only a housewife," she said. "Can you talk in a language that I can understand because those letters mean nothing to me?" She was a small white haired old lady, so Dr. Kennedy apologized and the rest of the meeting was made very understandable. I was told later that Marjorie understood everything, even the alphabetized codes, but she often played stupid in order to get government officials to explain themselves in elementary language that could not be misinterpreted. Then when she went home she would write them a letter thanking them for the meeting and reviewing substantive things that were discussed and agreed to at the meeting.

From that time on, when in Washington DC, I often introduced myself to government officials as a "housewife from Connecticut" so they would lower their expectations of my knowledge and expertise, forcing them to explain things at an elementary level. Since so many government people were older white upper middle class men, I simply played into their expectations that a woman's capabilities did not extend beyond cooking, cleaning and raising children.

*

While I struggled to address the orphan drug problem, other parents took drastic measures to try and provide help to their children. A woman in Los Angeles, Muriel Seligman, had a teenage son with a very bad case of Tourette syndrome. Adam Seligman had many involuntary movements but he also had coprolalia, involuntary cursing. To top it off, Adam Seligman could not stop spitting, which made it a challenge to take him anywhere in public.

When she heard that my son had been successfully treated with pimozide, Muriel found a doctor in Los Angeles who would write a prescription for the drug, and by hook or crook she would get the prescription to Canada where a pharmacy would fill the prescription. Pimozide was actually on the Canadian market, so Tourette patients in Canada were able to use it.

*

When I started working at the TSA in 1980, my office was not much bigger than a cubby hole. The room was actually part of the bathroom; there were walls and a door around the toilet, but the sink was behind my office chair. So people exiting the bathroom would stop to wash their hands behind me. I could only hope they would keep the toilet door closed when they flushed so it would not be heard over my telephone handset, and they would be careful enough not to splash water on me from the sink. I wondered very often whether all non-profits lived like this, but there was not much I could do about it. One day I got a phone call from Muriel Seligman; it was sometime in 1980. She was very upset, and explained that a friend was going to Canada so she asked him to bring back pimozide because it worked well on her son Adam. But at the airport, the U.S. Customs Service confiscated the drug because it was not approved by the FDA.

What should she do, she asked? I told her the only thing I could think of: "Call Your Congressman" I said, "By the way, who is your Congressman?"

"Henry Waxman" said Muriel.

Representative Henry Waxman was the Chairman of the Subcommittee on Health and the Environment, which had jurisdiction over most federal health-related legislation. He was known as a brilliant policymaker who delved into health-related issues so completely that his staff people became virtual experts on issues such as Medicare, Medicaid, childhood vaccines, the FDA, tobacco, generic drugs, etc.

When Henry Waxman heard that one of his constituents was affected by the orphan drug problem he assigned one of his knowledgeable staff members, Bill Corr (who became the Deputy Secretary of the U.S. Department of Health and Human Services during the Obama administration) to examine the issue and see what needed to be done.

At the time of Muriel's phone call to me, Congresswoman Elizabeth Holtzman of Brooklyn was already delving into the orphan drug issue. Her constituent, Sharon Dobkin, had a rare disease called postanoxic myoclonus. It is a neurological disease suffered by people who have been deprived of oxygen to the brain. Throughout her life, Sharon had serious allergies and at one point she had stopped breathing long enough to suffer brain damage. Even though she was only in her 20s, she could not care for herself due to myoclonus, and was put in a nursing home with elderly people and confined to bed. Sharon's doctor was Melvin Van Woert of the Mount Sinai School of Medicine in New York. He was a mild mannered compassionate research neurologist who specialized in movement disorders such as

Left to right: Congressman Henry Waxman (D-Ca), Sharon Dobkin of New York, Abbey Meyers (CT) sand Adam Seligman (CA) from the first orphan drug congressional hearing in 1980. Sharon suffered from postanoxic myoclonus and Adam had severe Tourette Syndrome.

Parkinson's disease, Tourette syndrome, myoclonus, etc. He figured out that a chemical called L-5HTP (levodopa- 5 hydroxytryptophan) could help myoclonus patients. It did in fact help them, and they were able to leave their beds. Since no manufacturer was willing to make the drug, Dr. Van Woert made it by hand, and his recovered patients came to his laboratory at Mt. Sinai to help him stuff the drug into capsules.

It was such an outrageous problem that Congresswoman Holtzman got involved to help Sharon. She designed and introduced to Congress, an Orphan Drug law that would have put the government into the drug manufacturing business. The government would give money to a pharmaceutical company to develop an orphan drug and get it approved by the FDA for sale in the United States. When the manufacturer sold the drug to patients the company would hand any profits from the drug back to the government. This would establish a revolving pool of money that the government could lend to other orphan drug manufacturers in the future.

When Holtzman's law was introduced the pharmaceutical industry knew it wasn't going anywhere, primarily because drug companies would fall on their own swords to prevent it from passing Congress. Business is in business to make money, they said, so why would they give their profits to the government? They refused to even comment on the proposed law because they would not even admit the orphan drug problem existed!

*

Bill Corr examined every conceivable aspect of the orphan drug problem. He wanted to speak to doctors and researchers, so I gave him the names of rare disease doctors and researchers. He then told me that Henry Waxman decided this is a big enough issue that warranted a congressional hearing. He invited Adam Seligman and me to testify about Tourette syndrome, and Sharon Dobkin and Dr. Van Woert to testify about myoclonus. He also invited pharmaceutical manufacturers to testify. They thanked him for the invitation but refused to send anyone to speak at the hearing, or to even sit in the audience.

I really had to wonder at the gall of an industry that is so powerful it can ignore a congressional Chairman's request, not to mention their customers who purchase the medicines that they make! Years later I watched Henry Waxman on TV asking the CEOs of tobacco companies to raise their right hand and swear to him that nicotine is not addictive. No industry should ever challenge the Chairman of a congressional committee because in the end there will be a mighty price to pay. But the pharmaceutical industry had tagged Waxman as a "Liberal", and they must have sensed satisfaction from ignoring him. Conservative Ronald Reagan was now the President of the United States, and he had made a laughing stock of "liberals" during his campaign, so snubbing Waxman was hardly a blip on the screen for the hugely profitable American pharmaceutical industry. After all, in 1980 liberal Democrats were a small minority in United States.

The Congressional hearing took place in June 1980. We walked into a large hearing room that was empty except for the four of us sitting at the witness table. In the audience were my husband Jerry, and Pat Eagan who ran the Washington DC chapter of the TSA, and her husband. The remainder of the audience in the cavernous hearing room was a sea of empty chairs and one unidentified young man sitting in the very last row.

At the start of the hearing Mr. Waxman made a point that he had invited the pharmaceutical industry's trade organization to testify, but they refused. Then he asked the four of us to tell our stories, which we did. They were compelling stories, and the pharmaceutical lobbyists were not there to claim we lied. After the hearing I asked Bill Corr, "What happens next?" He answered, "That's up to you. Get public opinion on your side, get newspaper and magazine stories about orphan drugs, and the public will eventually demand that something should be done."

We thanked Henry Waxman and Bill Corr, and we went home. For the four of us it felt good to take a heavy weight off our chests, but we could not predict that anything would happen because of our testimony. After all, no one of importance was there to hear it!

However, unbeknownst to us, the young man in the back of the room was a reporter for the *Los Angeles Times*. He would write a very brief story on the hearing that would be buried in the middle of the paper. But that story would be read by someone who had the power to ensure that the entire country would learn about the orphan drug problem and the struggles of people with rare diseases.

Chapter 3

The Road to Passage

"The good die young, but not always. The wicked prevail, but not consistently."

American actress, Helen Hayes

When I returned to my office after the congressional testimony, two things happened: first there was a phone message from a vice president of McNeil Labs asking to meet with me, and second there was a phone call from a producer of a popular television show. There were also several phone messages about an article in the *Los Angeles Times* on June 27, 1980 about the testimony of Adam Seligman to the U.S. Congress regarding "orphan drugs."

*

I agreed to meet with the McNeil Labs VP in the office of Bill Pearl, the man who had initially loaned an office to the TSA. I knew the pharmaceutical company executive should not be told to come to the storefront because my bathroom office was not big enough, nor appropriate for guests. So a few days later I went to the meeting place and was surprised to find three executives from McNeil Labs and its parent company, Johnson & Johnson (J&J).

They had apparently read my testimony about pimozide, and they wanted to talk to me and explain the pharmaceutical business and the difficulties of drug development. They explained that it is a very complicated and highly regulated business, and it is expensive to jump through the hoops that FDA requires to prove a new medicine is safe and effective. Mr. Pearl identified with their problems conforming to government rules because he was a businessman, but his business was automobile parts, not human lives. I couldn't help feeling resentment that he was not thinking in terms of patients with TS, even though his own son suffered from severe TS for many years. I was wary when I heard that the executives wanted to meet with me. I knew that pharmaceutical companies had resisted most laws that applied to their industry – even laws that were designed to save people's lives.

Until the 1960s pharmaceutical manufacturers were required to prove only that a medicine was safe, but in the 1960s the drug thalidomide caused horrendous birth defects, and as a result, in 1962, Congress passed the Kefauver-Harris Amendments to the Food, Drug and Cosmetics Act (FD&C Act). That amendment required drug companies to also prove their drug is effective, and that it does what it claims to do on its label. It costs a lot of money to prove effectiveness of a medicine because such proof requires testing in humans (clinical trials) and, therefore, pharmaceutical companies felt they should only develop treatments for the largest and most profitable markets, the visitors explained.

The Kefauver-Harris Amendments was signed by President John F. Kennedy in October 1962. Senator Estes Kefauver (D-Tenn) and

Representative Oren Harris (D-Ark) co-sponsored the bill in light of the erupting European tragedy over thalidomide, a sedative that was used to treat morning sickness in pregnant women.

Senator Kefauver held the first hearing on this subject in 1959 when he was chairman of the Senate Subcommittee on Antitrust and Monopoly. Until then, he had focused on drug pricing and marketing, believing that American consumers were paying too much for drugs that were not proven to be effective. He introduced legislation to require truth in labeling and marketing of pharmaceuticals, but it was not enacted by Congress. He also broke a monopoly of antibiotic manufacturers who conspired together for high pricing.

A drug manufacturer, the William S. Merrell Company, wanted to market thalidomide (brand name-Kevadon) in the United States, but an FDA Medical Officer, Frances Kelsey, Ph.D., M.D., refused to approve the drug because of insufficient safety data. By 1962, the catastrophic effect of thalidomide on babies whose mothers took the drug in pregnancy was frightening. Thousands of babies had been born in Europe with missing or flipper-like arms and legs, and the common thread was that their mothers had taken thalidomide during pregnancy.

Since the FDA had not approved thalidomide for sale in the United States, it took some time to realize that the company had distributed the experimental drug to 1,200 American physicians, many of whom were treating pregnant women. FDA launched an immediate recall effort, but ultimately there were 17 births of deformed infants in the United States that were caused by thalidomide.

The public furor in the U.S. resulted in passage of the Kefauver-Harris Amendments which mandated several things: the law required pharmaceutical companies to prove the safety and effectiveness of their drug before it would be allowed on the American market;

mandated reporting of any serious side-effects from the drug after it is on the U.S. market; required "adequate and well controlled" clinical studies done by qualified experts to prove safety and efficacy; patient participants in research were henceforth required to sign an "informed consent" document truthfully describing the tests, risks and possible benefits of the drug being tested; required that unapproved drugs could not be distributed or sold in the U.S. in the absence of FDA approval; the creation of a retrospective review of drugs that reached the U.S. market between 1938 to 1962 to determine whether they were effective (this resulted in the withdrawal of hundreds of drugs from the U.S. market); required the FDA to create "Good Manufacturing Practices" (GMPs) that companies must follow and mandated FDA inspections of pharmaceutical factories; and gave the FDA control over drug advertising and accurate labels.

As a result of the Kefauver-Harris Amendments the FDA's drug approval process became the gold standard of the world, and American citizens came to expect that the government would protect them against unsafe and ineffective medicines. But many drug manufacturers continued to hope in the 1980s that somehow the Kefauver-Harris Amendments would be repealed so they could sell medicines without going to the expense of proving they are effective. I could not help wondering why Congress allowed the pharmaceutical industry, until the 1960s, to sell medicines that were not proven to be effective on the disease they were supposed to treat! Snake oil salesmen thrived for decades in that environment.

I collected antique medicine bottles and their labels were a joke because each one not only promised to treat dozens of human diseases, many also were good for your ailing horse or mule. I even had one medicine bottle that was clearly labeled "Cures Everything." But the main ingredients of the old medicines were primarily alcohol and opium. No wonder people felt better after taking them!

In 1938, Congress passed the Food, Drug and Cosmetics Act (FD&C Act), and the FDA was finally allowed to prohibit ingredients that were unsafe. Very quickly opium disappeared from the shelves of pharmacies and became a "prescription only" product. Proving a medicine was safe under the FD&C Act did increase the cost of drugs at the beginning of the 20th century, but the Kefauver-Harris Amendments greatly increased the cost of developing drugs because proof of efficacy takes years of tests on a large number of people. Unfortunately, the alternative of ineffective drugs would have cost the nation much more. However, the pharmaceutical industry continued to complain about government regulations as if they preferred to return to the snake oil days.

I understood the background of the Kefauver-Harris Amendments so I was not surprised, and unimpressed, when the executives from McNeil Labs pled their case in Mr. Pearl's office that day.

"Surely, you understand that we work for the benefit of our stockholders," one of the corporate executives said. "They invest in us because they want to share our profits. There is nothing wrong with earning a profit."

It became apparent to me that the men felt their stockholders were their customers, not the patients who bought their drugs. It also was apparent that he was talking down to me, so I decided to play the housewife.

"Well, you have to understand," I told the three pharmaceutical executives, "that I'm just a housewife so I don't know very much about high finance and business affairs. But, believe it or not, I do own stock in my retirement account, and I don't want to own any stock from a company that allows children to suffer. That's not only children with Tourette syndrome," I said. "But children with any rare disease, only because there's not enough of them to be profitable."I watched the faces of those powerful men suddenly droop. "I'm sure you have children and grandchildren," I said. "How would you feel if they were diagnosed with a serious disease and you couldn't get a treatment for them, not because there was no known treatment, but because no company felt it would be profitable enough to manufacture?" Then I reminded them that J&J has a wonderful corporate image of caring for children, even mercifully selling a shampoo that would not burn babies' eyes. "Is that all children, or just the ones that don't have a rare disease?" I asked.

When they left the meeting the three men were subdued. I did not expect to hear from them again because it was very obvious that they couldn't change my mind, so I would relentlessly pursue more newspaper, TV and magazine stories about the uncaring drug industry. Nevertheless, a few days later one of the men called me to let me know that corporate headquarters had changed its mind and McNeil Labs would develop pimozide for treatment of Tourette syndrome. I phoned Muriel Seligman and Dr. Shapiro immediately to let them know.

McNeil Labs did, indeed, develop pimozide for TS and did not wait for the Orphan Drug Act (ODA) to become law. They wanted me to know that the law was unnecessary. Thus pimozide, now known by the brand name Orap®, was not the first orphan drug to be manufactured, because the company never asked the government to designate it as an official orphan drug. Maybe they did it to shut me up or maybe they did it because they finally realized it was the right thing to do. I didn't care what their reasons were because in the end people with TS would be the beneficiaries of their decision.

"One down, a few thousand more orphan drugs to go" I thought.

*

The second important phone call came several days after I returned from the testimony. An office worker at TSA answered the call and put it on hold.

"Abbey," she said, "There's a man on the phone who says he is Maurice Klugman, Jack Klugman's brother, and he's a producer of the Quincy show."

I remember thinking "And surely I'm Mrs. Santa Claus."

I told her to put the call through and prepared to speak to a person who only wished he was Jack Klugman's brother. But it really was Maurice Klugman and he was a producer of the Quincy, M.E. TV show!

The weekly TV show was a popular mystery series about a medical examiner who solved crimes. Jack Klugman hired his brother as a producer because, as he said after Maurice died, his brother had not made a success of himself in the businesses that he dabbled in. But when Maurice went to work for the Quincy show he told Jack the program should not simply be a vehicle for entertainment, it should be used as a vehicle to educate the public about important health issues.

Maurice told me that he had a rare form of bone cancer, and he didn't expect to live much longer. He had just read the article in the Los Angeles Times about our congressional testimony for orphan drugs. Apparently, Maurice had called the reporter who gave him Muriel Seligman's phone number. In turn, Muriel told him to speak to me.

Maurice wanted assurance that if he could convince Jack to do a Quincy episode about Tourette syndrome and orphan drugs, we would help in any way they would need us. I told him we would give him all the technical help he would need. Shortly thereafter Jack agreed, and the program was aired on March 4, 1981. It was titled "Seldom Silent, Never Heard" and it depicted a teenager with Tourette syndrome who was murdered near a movie theater because he could not stop making noises and yelling inappropriate words in the theater. At the end of the program Jack announced that although the story and characters were fiction, the orphan drug problem was real.

Since the lead actor had virtually lived with Adam Seligman for several days, he copied Adam's symptoms beautifully. As a result, many people were diagnosed with Tourette syndrome because of the Quincy program. But literally thousands of people who saw the program wrote to Klugman about the rare disease they or their loved ones had, asking if he knew of any treatments for them, and offering their support to solve the orphan drug dilemma.

The Quincy show staff put those letters into large mail sacks and sent them to me. When the postman arrived he looked like Santa Claus unloading sacks of toys from his sled. I had to quickly create a system of volunteers to help read each letter and respond.

The first thing I did was create a mailing list of all the people who wrote to Jack Klugman about the orphan drug problem. When we needed letters going to Congress, these people would be able to write or phone their elected officials to urge passage of orphan drug legislation. Secondly, I needed volunteers to read the thousands of letters and see who was simply writing to help the orphan drug effort, and who was asking for help with their own rare disease. Then those letters were separated into groups. If they were writing about a rare skin disease, for example, I sent those letters to a skin disease support group because they had medical advisors who would know how to answer that letter, or where to refer the letter writer.

It took months to sort it all out, and then it would start again when summer repeats were aired again on TV. Quincy shows were also aired in foreign countries, so each time it showed in a foreign language we would get letters written in a foreign language, even years later. We solicited help from high school foreign language teachers who volunteered their skills to translate the letters.

I worked with the writer of the Quincy episode on orphan drugs, Sam Egan, so he could understand the motivations and behaviors of all involved parties. He depicted a woman at the FDA wanting to do something, but powerless to do anything. She was modeled after Dr. Marion Finkel, who was a high level FDA official. She was frustrated by her inability to do anything without permission from the White House and Congress.

The problem had to be solved by Congress, but some politicians would never defy large donors from the drug industry who opposed any orphan drug legislation. Pharmaceutical companies were shown to be most concerned about their stockholders instead of patients. Of course the patients were stuck, as they say, between a rock and a hard place, and Jack Klugman depicted the conundrum.

I realized that all of the people writing in after the Quincy episode represented, collectively, a very loud voice. But what was the best way to ensure that their voice would be heard?

*

When my boys were little, I wanted to get them a cool new tricycle that had a big front wheel, and two small wheels in back. But all of the big-wheel bicycles were made out of plastic, and I felt that plastic could easily break and might cause the children to get hurt.

About a year later, I was walking through a store and saw a new big-wheel bike, but its body was made of metal and only the wheels were plastic. So I bought the metal big-wheel tricycle for David.

About a year later David was riding the bike in front of our house and it broke, not at a joint that could have been improperly welded, but the middle of a long piece of metal linking the seat area to the handle bars. When I examined the bike I thought it was really dangerous to have a little child on the bike when it broke in an area that could have severely hurt him. When Jerry saw the bike he agreed, and he thought I should write to the manufacturer to warn them their bike was not safe.

Photo taken just before Jack Klugman testified before Congress in 1982. The people are:

Standing L to R-- Rep. Ted Weiss (NY), Judy Wertheim of the Tourette Syndrome Association (TSA), Abbey Meyers (TSA), Jack Klugman, Dr. Melvin Van Woert of Mt Sinai School of Medicine (NY), Adam Seligman (Tourette Syndrome). Bottom row: Betty Teltsher (TSA) Sharon Dobkin (Myoclonus), Niss Ryan (Narcolepsy) and Marjorie Guthrie (Huntington's Disease).

So I wrote a letter to the bicycle company. They wrote back and thanked me for my letter; they apologized for the flaw in the bike, and sent us a whole new bike. A few weeks later I received another bike with an apology from a different department of the same company, and a few weeks after that we received a third new bike from yet another department!

"Wow," Jerry said. "You know how to write letters!"

After the congressional hearing and the Quincy episode, there was no better way to teach businesses and politicians not to deceive mothers. Letters and phone calls became my weapons of choice and I encouraged anyone who wanted to help to do the same.

*

Around this time in March of 1981, Bill Corr checked in and wanted to know how things were going. I explained that we were getting publicity all over the country, not only because of Quincy but because families were willing to tell their stories to local newspapers and TV stations. Congressman Ted Weiss of New York was taking on the orphan drug issue now that Rep. Elizabeth Holtzman lost her re-election bid to the House of Representatives.

Congressman Waxman wanted to hold another orphan drug hearing, and this time he was sure that the pharmaceutical industry would show up and testify. He was thinking about asking Jack Klugman to testify because that would guarantee the press and TV would cover the hearing. Although today it is almost commonplace for a celebrity to testify before Congress, it was almost unheard of in the early 1980s. Jack KIugman's appearance before Congress on the orphan drug issue was a huge deal!

The second orphan drug hearing took place in the House of Representatives in March of 1981. I spoke to Jack and his writer Sam Egan beforehand, and while it was very unusual for an actor to testify, Jack was willing to do it to help the cause. As we approached the hearing room on the day of the hearing I was shocked to see a long line of people hoping to get in because the hearing room was filled to capacity. In fact it was over-capacity because people were sitting in the aisles and leaning on walls.

Word had reached support groups about the hearing, and many of the people in the audience were patients with a wide spectrum of rare diseases. The rest of the audience was people from the pharmaceutical industry and media. The room was lit up by powerful television lights, and even Jack had to climb over people sitting in the aisles just to get to the witness table. Whereas at our previous congressional hearing only Henry Waxman was there, and one or two other Congressmen dropped by for a few minutes, at this hearing many Congressmen showed up and had questions, primarily because TV cameras were recording the testimony.

Klugman's testimony was tremendous. He said he was only an actor, not a doctor, and not an expert on orphan drugs. However, he could see that there were "no good guys and no bad guys in this scenario," so time shouldn't be spent on finding who to blame. But orphan drugs are a serious problem, he said, and only Congress could solve it.

Then people representing the pharmaceutical companies testified. Some emphatically insisted that there was no orphan drug problem, that industry has always developed drugs for even the rarest diseases. In other words, they implied that we were making the whole thing up. I silently wondered how many dead children they wanted to see before they would believe it.

But other pharmaceutical company executives rebelled against the party line and testified that there was indeed a problem and it needed a congressional solution. They said drug development is an expensive proposition, but for orphan drugs they wanted to at least earn back the money they would have to invest on research and development, while having a fair chance to earn a profit. They did not think anyone wanted a guarantee that their drug would be profitable, because they don't have any guarantee for the usual drugs that they develop. However, they simply wanted a chance to earn profit; if they could not earn a profit on products they develop, they would soon be out of business.

*

After the Klugman hearing, I was shocked to read an editorial in the *Wall St. Journal* asking: What is this world coming to when Congress invites an actor to testify? They made fun of Klugman and they tweaked Henry Waxman. After that day I never again bought another *Wall St. Journal*.

The fact is there would never have been an Orphan Drug Act without Jack and Maurice Klugman, and "liberal" congressman Henry Waxman, and if the editors of the *Wall St. Journal* did not understand how many lives the new law would save, and the successful new businesses that would flourish because of the law, they should apologize for their lack of foresight. But the *Wall St. Journal* may have simply followed the signals sent out by the trade group, Pharmaceutical Manufacturer's Association (PMA—now PhRMA), which vehemently opposed the law. *The Wall St. Journal* simply parroted that corporate point of view and did not carefully come to its own educated conclusions.

Maurice Klugman died of bone cancer in May of 1981. He was unable to see the Orphan Drug Act became law. But this was after he had convinced Jack to do other shows that had a great impact on public health, including one about a plane crash where many passengers needlessly drowned because airlines and airports were insufficiently prepared, a show about sudden infant death syndrome (SIDS), and a second orphan drug show about a young mother afflicted with postanoxic myoclonus.

In the years since the Quincy shows about orphan drugs, Jack Klugman suffered repeated bouts with throat cancer. The last time I saw him was when he came to our celebration of the Orphan Drug Act's 10th anniversary, in Washington DC, with his dear friend Tony Randall. The "Odd Couple" indeed!

Celebrating the 10th anniversary of the Orphan Drug Act in 1993, Jack Klugman (R) and Tony Randall (L) joined us in Washington DC. Jack and Tony co-starred in the popular TV comedy show "The Odd Couple" for several years in the 1990's, but it was Klugman's "Quincey, M.E." series in the 1980's that spurred enactment of the ODA.

Jack Klugman died at the age of 90, on Christmas Day, 2012. I know there is a special place in heaven reserved for him because his talent and compassion saved millions of lives.

Senator Nancy Kassebaum (KS)
credit: U.S. Senate Historical Office

Photo of former Senator Nancy Kassebaum (Kansas), who was the Senate sponsor of the Orphan Drug Act. She agreed to sponsor the legislation when she was visited by a husband and wife who explained the importance of the legislation for families with rare diseases. The wife had Huntington's disease when they made that visit.

When Henry Waxman introduced his bill, there was not a lot of excitement on the corporate side, but it greatly energized the patient community. Support groups sent out notices to their members advising them to contact their Senators and Representatives in support of the legislation. Of course Marjorie Guthrie was a major cheerleader for all of the neurological diseases, and she inspired a husband and wife in Kansas to visit their Senator, Nancy Kassebaum, to talk about the need for orphan drugs to treat Huntington's disease.

Senator Kassebaum, a Republican who was the daughter of famed politician Alf Landon (who ran against Franklin Roosevelt for the Presidency) later told me that her heart broke for the couple that came to visit her. The wife had Huntington's disease, and her body was in perpetual motion. "What can I do for you?" asked the Senator. The husband told her the Orphan Drug Act was in the House of Representatives, and we needed a Senator to sponsor the law in the Senate. Sen. Kassebaum put her staff person, Susan Hattan, on the issue, and a few days later Kassebaum introduced the Orphan Drug Act in the Senate.

Now we only needed an army of people to visit their elected officials and ask them to endorse (co-sponsor) the Orphan Drug Act. If we could get half of the members of the House and half of the members of the Senate to sign on as co-sponsors, we could very likely force the bill to come up for a Congressional vote.

*

When I first started going up and back to Washington DC for meetings, it greatly disturbed my conscience because of my young children. Eastern Airlines (which no longer exists) had started the Air Shuttle with flights to Washington DC from LaGuardia Airport in New York. I would drive to LaGuardia early in the morning, praying for good weather so there would be no delays. Eastern Airlines policy was that the Air Shuttle was like an air-taxi; you did not need a reservation, you just got on the plane and the stewardess would process your credit card so you bought your ticket on- board. If you were at the gate at the end of an hour and there was no seat empty for you, they would pull out another plane and get you to Washington even if the new plane was largely empty. But when President Reagan fired air traffic controllers in the early 1980s for going on strike, the whole system changed and there were no more air-taxis. And for a very long time there was no hope of ever being on time at airports!

Over the years the shuttle was sold several times to different airlines. Nothing in the air (except perhaps birds) was on time, you needed reservations, and flight cancellations occurred more frequently. I remember the torture of waiting for planes in bad weather, missing planes, wondering if the kids remembered to pack their lunch, sitting at witness tables in Congress and worrying if I would get home in time to do laundry, etc. Traveling was not a pleasant exercise for me, and my family paid a heavy price. Fortunately I could count on Jerry getting home before me, and out of necessity he would cook dinner for the family.

I could not spend a lot of time in Washington, but when I did, I always had a clear agenda with time limits. I had to separate what I was doing for orphan drugs from my work at the Tourette Syndrome Association, so when I got back to the TSA office I knew my desk would be piled high with backlogged work.

Every once in a while, I would be amazed at how much I had learned about science and medicine; two subjects that never interested me in school. Now suddenly out of necessity I was immersed in a world of enzymes and proteins, DNA and RNA, good laboratory practices, clinical trials, bioethics, etc. When I was a newcomer to the field of non-profit voluntary health agencies, it was like landing in a foreign country with strange languages and customs, not unlike a 22 year old American from Brooklyn landing in Pusan, Korea. One had to be immersed in the new culture before you could understand it and make a difference. Science and medicine are awesome challenges, especially when your knowledge begins at ground zero!

*

Marjorie Guthrie did not like the way I walked. I was too slow. So she tried to teach me the rhythm of walking on the sidewalks of Washington DC. I was honored that a Martha Graham ballerina was teaching me how to walk, but after a few steps I tended to lose the rhythm. It was hopeless to expect me ever to walk the streets of Washington with authority and grace. I was not privileged in my childhood to go to dancing school, and I certainly wasn't going to learn how to be graceful after having three children.

When Marjorie walked into a Congressman's office she sized up his age. If he was an older man, she introduced herself as Woody Guthrie's widow. If he was younger, she introduced herself as Arlo Guthrie's mother. She always got their undivided attention. In Washington DC, sometimes I would visit congressional offices alone, sometimes with people from other support groups and sometimes with people who had Tourette syndrome and their families.

Marjorie's advice was truly helpful in teaching me the nuances of dealing with elected officials. However, in some cases, no matter how much or how well I argued for the rare disease community some people never understood.

I remember walking into a congressional office with the mother of a child who had Rett syndrome, a devastating neurological disease that primarily affects girls. They cannot walk or talk, her daughter was in a wheelchair. We were talking to a female staff person who seemed annoyed that she had to spend time with us. The mother of the girl in the wheelchair said she didn't know how much longer her daughter would live. The staff person got quickly to her feet and said, "Don't throw dying babies at me, I'm sick and tired of hearing about them." Abruptly she left the room, leaving us so stunned we could not say anything for several minutes. Tears ran down the mother's cheeks, and mine.

*

Interestingly, even though the official drug industry stance on the Orphan Drug Act was to oppose it, individuals from the largest companies would pull me aside, or call me on the phone to say "keep on doing what you're doing." Even though their companies opposed the campaign for orphan drugs, workers at those companies knew that the law was needed and they hoped that we would be successful. They knew of drugs that their own companies had put aside because the marketing department felt it would not be profitable enough. They would attend meetings where speeches were made in opposition to the law, they would nod their heads in agreement, but they served as our anonymous cheering section throughout the struggle. That meant everything to me.

It also gave me special insight into the people who choose to build their career in the pharmaceutical industry. Many times they would tell me that they were drawn to the industry because they wanted to really make a difference to humanity by being involved in development of an important new therapy. In their mind they hoped to be involved in the equivalent of the Salk polio vaccine, or development of antibiotics at the beginning of WW II. Instead, too many pharmaceutical employees felt trapped when they were assigned to development of their company's 20th blood pressure drug or another sleeping pill. They didn't want to spend decades of their life on "me-too" drugs that didn't make a difference. They knew that most orphan drugs would be breakthrough treatments for untreatable, crippling and deadly diseases, and their lifetime of work could mean a great deal to the lives of those patients.

*

When Congressman Waxman wrote the Orphan Drug Act, he sent me a "discussion copy" and asked for my thoughts. This was before the Congressional hearing involving Jack Klugman.

In my mind, the orphan drug problem was a civil rights issue. Rare diseases are illnesses of a minority of citizens. Individually they have no political strength, but put them together and millions of Americans are affected. I knew that if the patient community had the collective power to get an orphan drug law enacted. But what should the law actually say if we could stay united?

I knew Congresswoman Holtzman's law, now sponsored by Rep. Ted Weiss, would not solve the problem because there would be no chance for companies to recoup all of their expenses and earn a profit on their orphan drug. Orphan drugs were primarily an economic problem and it needed an economic solution. We patients could not manufacture orphan drugs and the government is not a pharmaceutical manufacturer. We needed the drug industry to get involved because they knew how to do research on pharmaceuticals, develop and get the drugs through the FDA approval process, manufacture and market them. It was painfully clear that companies would not get involved unless they could earn a profit.

Congressman Waxman's solution created financial incentives that would entice companies into developing orphan drugs. He introduced his first version of the Orphan Drug Act (H.R.5238) in December 1981. He then held a congressional hearing on the legislation on

March 8, 1982. During this time, he had commissioned a study by Carolyn Asbury, who was a graduate student at the Wharton School in Pennsylvania, to question pharmaceutical companies about the type and number of orphan drugs they had developed and marketed. She was able to document that the U.S. pharmaceutical industry had developed only 10 orphan drugs over the preceding ten years that had not received government or university support during the research and development process.

The first draft of the law aroused intense discussions with pharmaceutical manufacturers, rare disease consumer organizations, academic researchers and government agencies. In the draft law that was finally passed by the House of Representatives late in 1982, the legislation contained the following provisions:

- The sponsor of the orphan drug could request that the FDA provide written recommendations on the types and numbers of studies that would be required before the FDA could review the drug. This could provide companies and researchers with tools to predict the time and resources that would be needed to develop the treatment.

- When a company requested the FDA to designate a drug as an "orphan drug," the FDA was empowered to do so if the Secretary of the Department of Health & Human Services (DHHS) found that the drug was for a disease or condition occurring so infrequently in the United States that there was no reasonable expectation that the development and distribution costs would be recovered from U.S. sales. This imprecise definition also made it clear that a disease that is prevalent in the rest of the world but rare in the U.S. could also qualify and receive the benefits of an orphan drug designation in the United States. Nevertheless, the absence of a clear definition of "rare" remained a problem until the law was eventually changed and a numerical definition was adopted (fewer than 200,000 people in the U.S.).

• Drugs that receive the official designation of an "orphan drug" must be made public so that consumers and medical professionals will know that the experimental treatment exists, and who is sponsoring the drug. Too often drug companies had historically insisted that this information was a "trade secret," and they did not want competitors to know what they were developing.

• An orphan drug that achieves marketing approval from the FDA will receive seven years of exclusive marketing rights from the day the drug is approved by the FDA if the drug is unpatentable. This quickly became the priority sentence that was changed one year after enactment because the majority of orphan drugs were patentable, but in many cases there was little remaining time left on their patents, or their patents were not strong enough.

• The law encouraged "open protocols" for clinical trials. This would allow physicians to request the experimental drug for patients who were unable to participate in a clinical trial, if there was no other satisfactory therapy available. The doctor and the drug company would still have to conform to the FDA's rules and reporting procedures for experimental drugs. This provision answered one of the major findings of the Asbury survey: Some companies never intended to develop their drugs for rare diseases, and allowed them to stay classified as "experimental" drugs indefinitely.

• The law would also create the DHHS Orphan Products Board, an intra-governmental committee composed of people representing various government agencies that conducted or supported medical research. The Board was supposed to promote development of drugs and medical devices for rare diseases and conditions. This body was responsible for submitting an annual report to Congress that would evaluate the federal government's implementation of the Act. (However, the Board stopped meeting after a few years.)

• Tax credits amounting to 50 cents of every dollar a manufacturer spent on human clinical trials was included in Waxman's initial law. However this provision caused numerous problems because any tax law must go through the congressional committees that are responsible for taxes, and Waxman was not a member of those committees. Additionally, the remaining 50 cents of every dollar spent on clinical trials would have been a deductible business expense, so each company could have deducted 73% of their clinical trial expenses, which raised the ire of many Senators and Congressmen.

• The law also contained a provision for the Secretary of HHS to award grants and contracts for the development of new drugs and medical devices for rare diseases. Congress was allowed to appropriate up to $4 million for this program that began when Congressman Jamie Whitten put aside $500,000 for orphan drug research grants. The program became one of the most productive research programs administered by the U.S. government with numerous drugs, biologics and humanitarian medical devices on the market today because of this program.

The bill passed the House of Representatives just before a Congressional recess was scheduled in 1982. If an Orphan Drug bill passed the Senate before the recess, any differences between the House and Senate legislation would be worked out in a House-Senate Conference Committee. Waxman went to the Senate to talk to Senators Hatch (UT) and Kennedy (MA), trying to convince them to pass a similar bill that could be voted on during the "Lame Duck" session after the November election. Senator Bob Dole (KS) was Chairman of the Senate Finance Committee so his cooperation was crucial to the survival of the tax credit provisions. The Senate negotiators dropped the tax credits in their bill and passed their version of the Orphan Drug Act on the last day of the pre-Congressional recess period.

Herculean negotiations between the House and Senate now ensued because the bill from the House of Representatives was not the same as the legislation that was passed by the Senate. I understand that Sharon Dobkin went to visit Senator Dole during this period, and while she was there the Senate bells started ringing loudly to alert elected officials about something. The loud bells triggered a myoclonus attack in Sharon while Senator Dole was in the room, and he changed his mind about the need for an Orphan Drug Act, but he still wanted the tax credits to be amended to a law related to taxes, not health. Senator Kassebaum's aid, Susan Hattan, spent many sleepless nights negotiating with staff from the tax writing committees, and they finally came up with a compromise that would prevent a major drain on the treasury. They decided that companies would have to choose between using the 50% clinical trials tax credit or the other 23% business tax credit, but no company could claim both. The provision was added to tax legislation, not to the Food, Drug and Cosmetics Act, and it was passed by Congress at the end of 1982.

On December 14, 1982, the compromise Orphan Drug Act passed the House of Representatives and on December 17 it passed the Senate. Since Congress adjourned for the Christmas holidays, if President Reagan did not sign the Orphan Drug Act by January

4th, the bill would be dead. The President was rumored to be planning to veto the bill and the members of Congress could not override his veto if they were not in session. So, it was all up to President Reagan. He was being advised not to sign the bill because of certain attached amendments, which had nothing to do with rare diseases or orphan drugs at all. Convincing President Reagan to change his mind on vetoing the bill was a colossal task and it took a lot of effort, creativity and persistence from supporters of the bill and the rare disease community as a whole.

Left to right: Congressman Ted Weiss (D-NY), Sharon Dobkin (NY), Congressman Henry Waxman (D-CA), and Abbey Meyers (CT) in the late 1980's.

*

After the Klugman hearing in 1981 we did everything to encourage publicity about orphan drugs, using local patients all over the country who were willing to go on TV or be the subject of newspaper stories. It was working very well and we hired a clipping service to review all articles printed about rare diseases and orphan drugs. In the beginning we saw one or two articles a day, but in time the clipping service was sending us 10, 20 or more articles per day from local newspapers and magazines. When the Orphan Drug Act finally passed the House of Representatives in 1982, the compromise bill was sent to the Senate for its approval. It stalled there for several months even though we continued to keep up pressure on all Senators, and the local media stories about the need for orphan drug legislation continued to encourage public support.

Even though I consider myself a lifelong history buff, like most Americans I was ignorant about the inner workings of the House of Representatives and the Senate. I had not known that any Senator can put a "hold" on a bill, which prevents the legislation from going before the full Senate for a vote. The name of the Senator who puts a hold on legislation does not have to be revealed. In fact, any Senator trying to stop a bill from being voted on usually employs much trickery to hide his identity.

Eventually we learned that Senator Alfonse D'Amato put a hold on the Orphan Drug Act, and since he was a New York Senator I phoned several rare disease charities based in New York City and told them the Senator's identity. They proceeded to have numerous patients, their friends and their family members, call Senator D'Amato's office and demand that he take his hold off the bill.

The reason for the hold had nothing to do with orphan drugs. The Orphan Drug Act had several amendments stuck on the end of it that had been attached to the bill when it went through congressional committees. When Senators identify a bill that is likely to get passed into law, they know that it is the perfect vehicle to attach a pet project to, even if their amendment has nothing to do with the main subject of the legislation.

One of the amendments attached to the Orphan Drug Act was known as "the Aspartame amendment." Aspartame is an artificial sweetener (now marketed under the brand names NutraSweet® and Equal®) that had a difficult time obtaining approval from the FDA. In fact, the controversial approval had taken so long that aspartame hardly had any patent time left, so lobbyists had succeeded in getting an amendment tacked onto the Orphan Drug Act through the Senate for 10 additional years of patent protection for the manufacturer of aspartame. However, the Reagan administration felt it was poor public policy to create a precedent of lengthening patents through lobbying (because it would send a signal to other companies that wanted to lengthen their patents), and Senator D'Amato objected to the patent extension because the company that manufactured saccharin, another artificial sweetener (marketed as Sweet'N Low®), was located in Brooklyn.

Within a few hours of Sen. D'Amato's staff opening their office, one of his staff members called me and requested that I stop people from tying up their phones. "The Senator," he said, "is taking his hold off the bill."

"Please thank the Senator," I said politely.

*

We still had to erase the holds from several other Senators, but the larger problem at the moment seemed to come from the Reagan administration. So I went with several support group leaders to visit the Assistant Secretary of Health and Human Services, Dr. Edward Brandt, Jr. We spoke to him for about 20 minutes.

One of the attendees was a lovely lady who suffered since her teenage years with narcolepsy. Because she would suddenly fall asleep without warning, she carried a tape recorder with her so if she missed anything that was said she could just listen to her tapes. She asked Dr. Brandt if he would mind if she taped the meeting and he said okay. At the end of the meeting, after we explained the need for the Orphan Drug Act, he admitted that as a physician he knew there was a desperate need for orphan drugs, but for political reasons he said, "Even though I can't support it, I won't oppose it." That gave us the green light because we now felt that the Reagan administration would not try to stop the bill.

*

After all but one Senator's hold was wiped away, we were feeling encouraged. But the rumor was that last Senate hold came from Senator Orin Hatch of Utah. To this day, I don't know for sure which Senator actually had the last stubborn hold on the orphan drug legislation, but it turned out to be the most problematic because it was there for several months and was not easily dislodged.

The American government had done atomic bomb testing during the 1950s in Utah and Nevada. Now in the 1980s there seemed to be a high prevalence of cancer cases identified in that area of the country and residents wanted to know if the atomic bomb testing was responsible. So in the rush to add irrelevant amendments to the Orphan Drug Act, a mandate was added for a federal study of cancer cases in Utah and Nevada, to determine whether they were related to atomic bomb testing.

People in the Reagan administration were alarmed by this amendment. What could happen if the study found that yes, there is a higher incidence of cancer in Utah and Nevada? It could open the federal government to lawsuits that may cost billions of dollars! The administration did not want the amendment to pass, and if that meant that the Orphan Drug Act went down the tubes, well too bad. After all of the work we did to clear away all of the obstacles, we were left with a stalemate that we could not influence because there was no relationship between orphan drugs and atomic bomb tests.

*

During the spring I received a phone call from Jack Klugman's writer, Sam Egan. Maurice Klugman's death from bone cancer had greatly saddened Jack. Now, almost a year later, Egan was curious about the fate of the Orphan Drug Act, "So how is it going? Do you think the law will pass this year?" I told him how we had cleared away a number of Senate holds, but now one Senator was unwilling to withdraw this last hold. I was told that Senator Hatch was the sponsor of the Utah/Nevada cancer amendment and for sure he wanted it to pass Congress, so why would he put a hold on the bill? I just didn't know. And ultimately no one could prove that Senator Hatch was actually preventing the Orphan Drug Act from reaching the Senate floor because even today, 30 years later, the act of Senators placing "holds" on legislation is still kept secret!

I mentioned that we even saw Dr. Brandt, the assistant secretary of Health and Human Services. "What did he say?" Sam asked. "He said, 'I can't support it, but I won't oppose it'," I answered. "I think it could mean the administration won't oppose it *if* it gets to the President's desk."

Sam Egan wrote another orphan drug script for the Quincy show. This episode was titled "Give Me Your Weak." It was about the orphan drug L-5HTP for myoclonus, and the story mirrored Sharon Dobkin's life. Sharon was now married and she just had a baby, but any loud noise (such as a telephone ring), made her jump and experience spasms.

Jack wanted the script to be about a Senator who had a hold on the Orphan Drug legislation, and he wanted the program to include a march on Washington with several hundred rare disease patients... not actors, real patients!

Sam asked me if I could get the patients, and I told him I was sure I could, but how would they get to Washington DC? After all, many were too sick to fly anywhere, and Washington DC would be very cold in the autumn when it would be filmed. "Don't worry," said Sam, "there's a street in Pasadena that looks just like Washington DC, so just find a few hundred rare disease patients in California."

When the episode about myoclonus and orphan drugs aired on October 27th, 1982, I thought the street in Pasadena looked just like Pasadena, but most of America thought it was a march of rare disease patients in Washington DC. The patients in the march carried hand written signs and they were so grateful for the opportunity to express themselves that they didn't really care that they were in Pasadena. Even today people who remember that episode of Quincy assume that the march really occurred and it took place in Washington DC!

The very last line in the program was when Quincy asked the Senator to remove his hold from the legislation. The Senator said, "I can't support it, but I won't oppose it."

Thanks to Jack Klugman, Sam Egan and the rare disease marchers in Pasadena, the very last hold was taken off the bill in the Senate.

During 1982 when the ODA was stuck in Congress, Klugman decided to do another "Quincy" TV show about orphan drugs. This show was modeled on Sharon Dobkin's story about Myoclonus, and Dr. Van Woert's orphan drug. The final scene of the TV program was supposed to be a March on Washington, so we contacted several hundred people with rare diseases and they held signs and marched, but NOT in Washington.....the producers and directors said there was a lovely street in Pasadena that "looks like Washington". So the patients marched in Pasadena, but even years later viewers continued to believe there was an actual march on Washington that got the ODA through Congress! Jack Klugman can be seen in the center of this photo among eager marchers.

The Orphan Drug Act passed the Senate before Congress went home for Christmas vacation. President Reagan had 10 days to sign the Orphan Drug Act into federal law. Then he left for vacation in Palm Springs. Out of all the joy from our series of victories, rumors started to reach us that the President had been advised not to sign the bill into law because that pesky amendment about cancer in Utah and Nevada could end up costing the American government billions of dollars. The struggle was not over yet!

*

An anonymous donor sent us a $10,000 gift which was enough to purchase advertisements in *The Washington Post* and the local newspaper in Palm Springs, California begging President Reagan not to veto the Orphan Drug Act. The advertisement asked him at Christmas not to act like "scrooge" to the millions of children with rare diseases who desperately needed the Orphan Drug Act. The ad was printed in the Palm Springs newspaper on December 31, 1982, and then it appeared in *The Washington Post*.

MR. PRESIDENT, PLEASE SIGN THE ORPHAN DRUG ACT

Dear Mr. President:

While you are back home for the holiday, we hope you will see this letter. We represent millions of Americans who suffer from over 2,000 rare diseases. Our only hope is the ORPHAN DRUG ACT. This bill, authored by Congressman Henry A. Waxman, is now sitting on your desk. It would give tax credits to drug companies that develop treatments for diseases that occur so infrequently that no company can expect to profit from the new drugs.

Just two weeks ago we rejoiced at the news that the ORPHAN DRUG ACT had passed both the Senate and the House of representatives by unanimous vote.

Shortly before Christmas we were shocked to learn that you are considering vetoing the ORPHAN DRUG ACT. This news turned our holidays from a time of joy to one of deep despair.

Without the ORPHAN DRUG ACT some of us are doomed to an early death. Some of us will be forced to face painful and disabling sicknesses with no hope of recovery or even relief.

Your signature before January 4th will bring America's great pharmaceutical industry into partnership with the Federal government on our behalf. It is incomprehensible to us and to our families that you would reject this opportunity to alleviate so much human suffering.

PLEASE SIGN THE ORPHAN DRUG ACT TODAY!

Sharon Dobkin Myclonus Families United	Judy Roser United Parkinson Disease Found.	Anne Kane Paget's Disease Found.
Dennis Smur Paralyzed Veterans of America	Barbara Landwher Nat'l Ichthyosis Found.	Abbey Meyers Tourette Syndrome Assoc.
Charlotte Drake Parkinson's Ed. Program	Dick Vodre Cystic Fibrosis Found.	Melvin Van Woert, M.D. Mt. Sinai Sch. of Medicine
John Chung Wilson's Disease Assoc.	Burt Diamond Nat'l Myclonus Found.	William Baird American Narcolepsy Assoc.
Ruby Horansky Nat'l Huntington's Disease Assoc.	Eames Bishop Amytrophic Lateral Sclerosis Society	Arlene Pessar Dystrophic Epidermolysis Research Foundation
George Brewer, M.D. Jess Thoene, M.D. Univ. of Michigan	Rose Marie Silva Internat'l Joseph Diseases Assoc.	Rita Kasky Nat'l Neurofibromatosis Foundation
Marjorie Guthrie Comm. to Combat Huntington's Disease	Thor Hanson Nat'l Multiple Sclerosis	Rubin Bakin Gaucher's Disease Internat'l Registry

*Organizational Affiliation listed for identification purposes only.

The advertisement asking President Reagan not to veto the Orphan Drug Act. (December 31ˢᵗ, 1982)

While the Reagans were in California someone was able to convince a movie star friend and tennis partner of Mrs. Reagan to talk to her about the need for the law. This conversation took place during a tennis game and I'm sure it was another important factor in changing the President's mind.

*

When he returned to Washington at the beginning of January, President Reagan signed the Orphan Drug Act into law at the White House. There was no signing ceremony, no photographs, and no souvenir pens passed out to attendees, just a statement that the President signed the Orphan Drug Act on January 4th, 1983. It became Public Law 97-414 (P.L.97-414).

The White House issued President Reagan's "signing statement," which was seven paragraphs long, a few days after he signed the bill. Five of the paragraphs explained rare diseases and the lack of treatment for them. He agreed that financial incentives were needed to attract the pharmaceutical industry to orphan drugs. Then he addressed the radiation amendment that was attached to the law which he objected to:

"I am signing this legislation despite the inclusion of a provision about which I have grave reservations. Section 7 of the bill directs the Secretary of Health & Human Services to publish tables showing a causal relationship between radiation exposure and subsequent cancer. The relationship between cancer and low levels of ionizing radiation has long been the subject of research by scientists throughout the world. Despite this intense interest, there is as yet no consensus among radiation experts in relating human cancers and exposure to low levels of radiation."

By the time of Marie Curie's death in 1934, scientists had recognized that radioactivity could cause cancer. This was at least 11 years before the first atomic bombs were dropped on Hiroshima and Nagasaki. Of course, the high incidence of cancer in Japanese survivors of the atomic bomb blasts reaffirmed that nuclear explosion left radioactive materials that could remain dangerous for millennia. However, during the Cold War, the United States continued to test atomic bombs in sparsely populated western desert areas such as Nevada. States close to Nevada such as Utah felt endangered from radioactive fallout from the bomb tests.

President Reagan, however, was known to cast aspersions on scientific findings that he disagreed with. Most notably he absolutely refused to admit that acid rain was killing forests, that the world was warming, and that AIDS had the potential to become a major public health threat. His doubts about the link between radiation and cancer flew in the face of general scientific knowledge. In fact, the public would have liked to know what the "safe" level of radiation is when we get dental x-rays, mammograms, etc.

I do not know if the government ever published the tables showing a link between radiation exposure and cancer. I do know, however, that Marie Curie died of cancer and she was the first to suggest that radiation, which caused cancer, also had the potential to cure it.

*

Years later Dr. Brandt told me that before the President signs a bill, a group of people gather at the White House to provide advice on whether the President should sign the legislation or veto it. At that meeting Dr. Brandt spoke on behalf of the Orphan Drug Act, but other political attendees all voted against the President approving it. They feared the Nevada/Utah study could cost the nation billions of dollars in the future, and they were very opposed to the precedent of a patent extension for aspartame. Dr. Brandt told me he left the meeting expecting President Reagan to veto the bill.

"I don't know what happened after that meeting," he said, "and I don't know what you did to change the President's mind. But when he signed it I was just as surprised as you were, and just as pleased" he told me.

*

I remember driving home from work that evening. People had been sending me flowers and champagne all day at the office so the car was full of roses and wine bottles. When I drove up the driveway the children came running down the stairs and flew into the garage. I got out of the car announcing, "It passed. It finally was signed by the President."

My children said, "Oh, that's why you're late. We're so hungry. When will supper be ready?"

Children have a way of bringing everybody back to reality.

*

In the years following 1983, Senator Hatch has often been given credit many times by the press for being one of the authors of the Orphan Drug Act. When one reporter makes a mistake and credits the wrong person for something, other reporters copy that mistake until it comes to be believed as true. However, it was Senator Kassebaum who was the Senate sponsor of the Orphan Drug Act and she fought like a tiger to get the bill on the floor of the Senate for a vote. Nancy Kassebaum, a Republican from Kansas, was a breath of fresh air to anyone who noticed that the Senate was composed of a sea of white males who hardly understood the way women analyze and solve problems.

Senator Hatch, on the other hand, was the Senate sponsor of Henry Waxman's generic drug law, the Drug Price Competition Act, which became known in Washington short-hand as the "Waxman-Hatch law" in the House, and the "Hatch-Waxman law" in the Senate.

That law was passed in 1984, one year after the Orphan Drug Act became law. The Hatch-Waxman law made lower cost generic drugs available to American patients, substantially lowering the cost of healthcare for years to come.

Additionally, a few months later, President Reagan gave a speech to the American Medical Association (AMA) taking credit for passage of the Orphan Drug Act. As my mother used to tell me, "All things come to he or she who waits."

*

Chairman Waxman was determined to have a party to celebrate passage of the Orphan Drug Act. He rented one of the big empty rooms in the Capitol and had a caterer fill a buffet table with luscious food, he invited his colleagues, congressional staff and leaders of the rare disease community. As swarms of people came in I noticed that they dutifully lined up to thank Henry Waxman and his staff, but then a line of people were lining up to congratulate me, of all people. I kept telling them I don't deserve any recognition, I wasn't the one who got the law passed. It was all the patients who called and wrote to their Congressmen and Senators. And it was Klugman who got people involved who didn't even have a friend or family member with a rare disease. Nothing would have happened without them.

On that day, I became aware of a growing myth on Capitol Hill about the Housewife from Connecticut. They told each other, "She's no housewife" but I knew I really was. I simply honed skills attained in the PTA and Scouts to fight City Hall on a larger scale, all the while hoping I would get home in time to do laundry or cook.

It was a complicated time and I always worried whether my family was given as much attention and love as they deserved. But one thing I knew was, if they or their loved ones ever needed a treatment for a rare disease, their likelihood of obtaining it was greatly improved!

However, I was soon to learn that the passage of a law does not ensure the enforcement of a law. Pharmaceutical companies could simply ignore the law if they wanted to and people with rare diseases would continue to suffer. What good would the Orphan Drug Act be if pharmaceutical companies did not take advantage of all it offered? We needed to develop a mechanism that would give academic medical researchers a voice in commercial discussions. The medicines we needed were mainly created in academia, but academic doctors did not know how to elicit the interest of drug companies.

Although the passage of the Orphan Drug Act was a major victory, the battle was not over. The industry had to be made to understand the benefits that are conveyed by the law and the people who did take chances on rare disease treatments needed to be supported. I realized that the struggle would go on and that we needed to continue behaving as a coalition of patient support groups. But ultimately, who would benefit from the blessings of the Orphan Drug Act if they could not obtain the treatments because they have no health insurance?

Chapter 4

NORD

"Hope is like a road in the country; there never was a road, but when many people walk on it the road comes into existence."

The Wisdom of China and India - Lin Yutang

I never imagined as a young girl that I would help to start and run a national nonprofit organization as an adult. I had known since a very young age exactly what I wanted to be when I grew up – an artist. Nonprofit corporations had never crossed my mind.

I had wanted to make my living by drawing, painting, sculpting – it didn't matter which. Many teachers tried to discourage me because they felt it would be very hard to earn a living in art. So, during high school I decided to study advertising design in a community college which would enable me to make a living in commercial art. My aim was to spend the least amount of money on tuition (since my mother could not afford tuition) and graduate quickly (within 2 years). I needed to start earning a salary quickly to help my mother and also to afford art supplies so I could continue painting in my spare time.

My mother had raised my sister and I alone after our father disappeared. He simply never came home. She was always told that any man in her office who had similar education and experience, and did the same job as her, would be paid more than her simply because he was a man. Men were expected to support their family, so it was generally accepted that they deserved higher salaries than women. But when I was 3 years old, and my sister was 6, our father deserted the family. Our mother was raising her two daughters by herself, as a bookkeeper and it apparently did not matter to her employers that she was also supporting a family because, after all, she was a woman! Therefore, my mother could not afford to send me or my sister to college. Nevertheless, I knew that education was the key to my future because I could not accept the discrimination that had held my mother down during her entire adult life.

Community colleges were a new concept in the 1960s, and besides being far less expensive than 4 year colleges, I could get an Associate's degree (Associate in Applied Science) in only 2 years. I was able to earn enough money on school vacation days as a telephone switchboard operator and I paid reduced tuition for keeping my grades up. After graduation I held jobs at advertising agencies and a package manufacturer, and when I married Jerry I was an Assistant Art Director at a big corporation, the American Chicle company, which manufactured many brands of chewing gum.

*

However, advertising design required that I ignore ethics when I tried to convince consumers to buy something that they didn't want or need. For example, when I was a commercial artist designing plastic packages, my boss gave me an assignment for a pantyhose package. I went to a store that sold many brands of pantyhose to see what those packages looked like. Then I went to work designing a package that would stand out from the rest while being tastefully designed. When

I finished the package I brought it to my boss and asked for the next assignment. She dug into a pile on her desk and handed me my new assignment – another pantyhose package for a different brand that was manufactured by the same pantyhose company.

I asked myself, "What's the point?"

I could only conclude that there was no point to anything I was designing. Who really cared which pantyhose brand sold more than other brands? The products in the packages were all the same, the profits from sales all went to the same company and I've never met a woman who loved one brand of pantyhose over another. In fact, most women hated wearing pantyhose!

Many of the people I've met in the pharmaceutical industry have felt that their life's work actually meant something to society. Keep in mind that I did not meet the average person working in an average drug company that made average drugs; when there are dozens of anti-hypertension drugs on the market, or another decongestant for the common cold, or lifestyle drugs like Viagra, making another one to compete in an already busy marketplace can seem like a pointless task. But when those same workers are dealing with an orphan drug, for a disease that has been historically hopeless, untreatable and deadly, they wake up every morning knowing that people's lives are depending on them doing a good job.

Time and again I saw these people move from one drug company to another, staying with orphan drugs or starting a new company solely devoted to orphan drugs. Time and again, I've seen CEOs retire, only to return a few years later to start a new pharmaceutical or biotechnology company devoted solely to orphan drugs. As one of them told me, "Once it's in your blood you can't get orphan drugs out of your system."

I know what they mean. I can understand them only because in my youth I wasted precious creative time and energy designing pantyhose packages. The irony is all of the pantyhose brands that I worked on came from the same factory, so it did not matter one iota which brand sold more than the others.

*

After the passage of the Orphan Drug Act, orphan drugs and rare diseases were definitely in my blood. And, in the summer of 1982, about 6 months before the Orphan Drug Act was signed into law, I held a barbeque in my backyard with several rare disease leaders including Marjorie Guthrie (Huntington's disease), Niss Ryan (narcolepsy), John Chung (Wilson's disease), Sharon Dobkin (myoclonus), and several others. Marjorie, who had been married to the quintessential American cowboy, a man who had idolized the American landscape ("This Land is Your Land, This Land is My Land"), did not like the bugs that flew and crawled in grassy New England backyards, so she wanted to know the questions immediately in order for her to be able to get everyone to agree on an answer—quickly, so she could escape the yard by finding refuge in my kitchen.

The question was: what do we do when the Orphan Drug Act is enacted into law? We had functioned as an effective coalition. Should we just disband the coalition or should we formalize it, and apply for nonprofit corporate status?

Marjorie said that she had spent several years working on hereditary disease legislation in a state Capitol, and when it passed the group of genetic disease charities said, "Mission Accomplished" and went home. But when the lobbying stopped the legislature never appropriated any money for the law, so nothing at all was accomplished. Thus she felt the orphan drug coalition should stay intact, incorporate as a nonprofit, and continue to monitor the implementation of the law; make certain that the government, the pharmaceutical industry and academic scientists will do what the law intended. A vote was taken and everyone agreed.

"What will we call the new charity?" I asked. More time was spent discussing possible names than was spent deciding whether or not we would disband. Finally, we all agreed on "National Organization for Rare Disorders." Why did we use the word "disorders" rather than "diseases"? Sharon felt that the word "disease" may imply that the conditions are contagious, whereas she felt "disorders" would not be interpreted as contagious to other people. Others agreed with Sharon. Citing the acronym, NORD, we raised our cups of diet soda and clinked plastic glasses: "Now we are the nerds from NORD," I announced.

*

I learned almost immediately that the competitiveness and territorialism that is rampant in the for-profit world also existed in the nonprofit world. I would frequently be forced to negotiate and compromise with groups that had the same objectives and should have been working together.

Several months after the barbecue, Marjorie phoned me and suggested that perhaps we should not go ahead and incorporate the new nonprofit. I asked her why and she said there was a coalition for neurologic diseases that had been lobbying successfully for years to increase the budget of the National Institute for Neurological Diseases and Stroke (NINDS), which was one of the National Institutes for Health (NIH). Someone from that coalition had called and asked Marjorie to stop NORD from moving forward because they were afraid that NORD might lure their members away.

I assured Marjorie that could not possibly be true because the coalition represented only neurological diseases, whereas NORD would represent all rare diseases, only some of which were neurological. Additionally, the mission of their coalition was a single focus – getting Congress to appropriate money for research on neurological diseases, some of which were rare and some of which were quite prevalent (e.g., stroke, Alzheimer's disease, etc.). NORD's mission was based on the concept that a rising tide lifts all boats and that any increase in research funding should not be based on politics or how common a disease is. Research should simply be funded because the science is good and the scientists are capable.

Additionally, NORD's focus would not be on research funding at the NIH. Our concern related to products that evolve out of successful research in the public and private sectors, and moving those products through the FDA so that patients can get them at local pharmacies. Thus we would focus more on the FDA at the end of the process than on NIH at the beginning of the process.

Silently, however, I thought about the comment years before in the Korean orphanage: "If you take all of my children, I will have no business." Were the people working at health related companies, even disease charities, worried that if new treatments and cures become available to patients then their business might suffer? Then I chided myself for becoming too paranoid and cynical. After all, the March of Dimes had started out to cure polio, but instead, they funded research on a vaccine that *prevented* polio. But they didn't go out of business; they simply changed their mission to promote research on the health of pregnant women and the health of babies.

Marjorie had discovered there was a malignant tumor in her intestines, she had it removed thinking she would quickly recover and could carry on her crusade against Huntington's disease. But when she called me about the problem with the neurological disease coalition, she was weak and obviously had no strength to carry out any new skirmishes. She told me she would set up a meeting for me with Sylvia Lawry, the founder of the National Multiple Sclerosis Society. "Bring anyone you want to that meeting," she said. "And explain to Sylvia what you just told me."

I don't remember how many of us went to meet Sylvia at her New York office. She had started the National MS Society when her brother had been diagnosed with MS during the 1940s, and she was told there was no treatment available. So she put a notice in the classified ads of *The New York Times* saying, "Multiple Sclerosis. Will anyone recovered from it please communicate with patient." What she realized afterwards was that some people do go through remissions of MS symptoms, but symptoms usually come back again and again as the disease waxes and wanes. She also realized that the MS community required a coordinated effort to promote and finance research into the causes of and treatment for MS. So she created the National Multiple Sclerosis Society.

At the time of our meeting there still was no treatment for MS on the horizon, but Sylvia felt there was some progress in advancing the basic knowledge about the disease which would eventually lead to treatments. She was right! And she knew in her heart that treatments for MS would be developed only if the Orphan Drug Act became law.

We explained to Sylvia that NORD would be no threat to the neurological coalition, and that we would not be lobbying for research funding at NIH. The orphan drug legislation, if it passed, would have an FDA grant program for clinical research on orphan drugs that would require our attention, but the FDA's appropriations from Congress were far removed from the NIH budget. In fact the

FDA's appropriations went through an Agriculture Appropriations committee which was more involved in fish-farming and diseases of peach and apple trees, than it was concerned about human health.

Politicians felt that appropriations for NIH research was always a good deed that constituents appreciated, but appropriations for the FDA were in support of a "regulatory" agency, which corporations do not appreciate. In fact, I reminded Sylvia, when a treatment for MS is eventually being developed it will likely qualify for the benefits of an orphan drug designation. The estimated prevalence of MS at that time was around 180,000 cases in the U.S., and I was trying to get the government to define a rare disease as an illness affecting fewer than 200,000 people in the United States.

In the end Sylvia agreed we would be no threat to the neurological coalition, and she wished NORD the utmost success. I was pleased to simply meet Sylvia Lawry, a legend in her own time. She phoned Marjorie to let her know the whole matter was put to rest.

*

Marjorie died from cancer on March 13, 1983 just two and a half months after the Orphan Drug Act was signed by President Reagan and became federal law. I was relieved that she lived long enough to see another accomplishment in her long list of accomplishments. Marjorie Guthrie was a great lady and an enduring model for leaders of other rare disease support groups.

In January 1983, we began the legal process of incorporating NORD and applying to the IRS for non-profit corporate status. It took several months for the process to be concluded.

Ruby Horansky, of the National Huntington's Disease Association, the organization that competed with Marjorie Guthrie's charity, was elected the first President of NORD. I could not be an officer because of my work at the Tourette Syndrome Association, but I did agree to serve on NORD's Board of Directors in a non-officer position. Ruby gave us a corner of her office for a desk and chair.

From 1983 to October 1985, we operated NORD as volunteers out of Ruby Horansky's Huntington's disease office on lower Broadway in New York City. The only staff person was a part-time college student who would send information to appropriate people on the Board of Directors or the Medical Advisory Board, whose members volunteered their time to take care of medical issues that were doled out to them. Increasingly, NORD was getting questions from the public about rare diseases, and because each member organization had a Medical Advisory "Committee" or "Board", questions we could not answer were sent to those medical experts.

The standard reply to questions about a rare disease was to mail out a copy of a page in a medical book, or a journal article about that disease. Inevitably, however, the people we sent the articles to could not understand the technical language. They would phone the office and ask us to explain the article.

Parents or individuals might receive a diagnosis (often after several years), but there was little or no understandable information about the disorder. Sometimes a physician might explain that they'd heard about this disease in medical school but knew nothing about it. This was before the Internet and people simply couldn't "Google it." Until they got in to see a specialist, they usually had been given nothing but generalities about their or their child's diagnosis. There simply wasn't anywhere to go that offered rare disease information that wasn't written in medical terminology.

It did not take very long before we recognized that the biggest need of the patient community was understandable medical information.

*

I had been working at the Tourette Syndrome Association since 1980. By 1985 the temporary 11 month job had turned into 5 years, and I had put 40,000 miles every year on my car. On the long rides home I was so tired I felt it would be best to leave the TSA and do nothing for a while except paint and read the books that I did not have time to read while working. And if I went back to work I wanted to be closer to my children so when they needed me I could get home quickly.

I attended a meeting in NYC with Bill Haddad and his assistant, Dee Fensterer. Bill Haddad was the chairman of the Generic Pharmaceutical Industry Association (GPIA). While the multi-national, brand name pharmaceutical industry dragged its feet on orphan drugs, the generic industry stepped to the plate immediately, led by Bill Haddad.

This particular meeting with Bill was to talk about the possibility of creating a rare disease computerized database. A university professor at the meeting said she could do it for about $200,000 a year. My eyes rolled up in my head because she was so far away from reality I was not looking forward to the rest of the discussion. Besides the outlandish price, I knew if a university professor was going to manage the database it would be written in technical medical language and patients who needed the information would not benefit from a database they could not understand.

On my way home I gave Dee a lift to her office. She was a really nice person so we talked about many things, both personal and professional. She asked how I was doing with my hectic schedule and travel, I replied that I was so exhausted, and so conflicted about my Tourette work which had to be separated from the orphan drug work, I was thinking about retiring. "You can't retire," Dee exclaimed, "we need you too much. The Orphan Drug thing needs you too much." She then asked if she and Bill Haddad could find the money for us to open a NORD office where it would be convenient for me, would I consider running the organization.

"Truthfully," I answered, "I would only consider running it if I could put the office near my house in Connecticut so I won't waste half my day traveling to and from my job." "Okay," Dee replied, "I'll talk to Bill and we'll see what we can do."

At the next meeting of the generic drug trade group Bill Haddad passed the hat and told people he wanted each of them to chip in so the generic companies would give $30,000 to NORD. Then he called me to say I needed to rent an office, wherever I wanted the office to be. Armed with the first year budget of $30,000, I made plans to open the office in Connecticut and resigned from the Tourette Syndrome Association. I left the TSA in good shape and they were able to continue the patient-oriented programs that I started.

*

I found inexpensive office space in Danbury, it was in the basement of a shopping center and the landlord had split it up into offices. There were no windows because it was underground, and I worried what might happen in the case of fire. There were several exits leading directly up to street level so I thought it might be a good place to start until we could afford better accommodations. I gave the real estate agent a deposit and let our Board of Directors know that I rented office space in Danbury.

A few days before we were scheduled to move in, I received a phone call from the landlord whose office was in New York City. He asked me about the type of business NORD was and I explained it was a charity for people with rare illnesses. Then he said, "Well I won't sign this lease unless you sign an addendum saying no one with AIDS will come into your office."

We had known about AIDS for several years because it precipitated a lot of publicity and was actually very rare at that time. Drug companies wanted to know if AIDS would qualify as an orphan disease, and it did. The FDA did designate the first drug for AIDS, "AZT", as an orphan drug, and that opened the way for other companies to at least look at the AIDS virus as a possible therapeutic area. Nevertheless, people in crowded cities tended to be paranoid about catching the HIV virus by simply standing near someone with AIDS, because they did not understand it could only be transmitted through bodily fluids. The public's fear was palpable.

I tried to remain calm and explained to the landlord that there was no risk of getting HIV from a person you simply talk to, and that he was needlessly discriminating against a group of disabled people who could not transmit their disease by walking into a room. "How can I guarantee that the postman or the UPS driver who may deliver a package doesn't have the HIV virus?" I asked. But that argument fell flat because the landlord's terror of AIDS was beyond reality.

I knew I wasn't going to win and ended the phone call with, "I'm going to sue you." But there was no federal law protecting people with disabilities from discrimination at that time. I could only add it to my "to do" list. This type of discriminatory attitude remained legal until the Americans with Disabilities Act (ADA) became law in 1990.

Fortunately, I contacted a well-known NY lawyer, Richard Goldberg, who cared about NORD's mission. He had told me he would volunteer his time if we needed him. I explained what happened with the landlord, he was so incensed he said, "Don't worry. I'll take care of it." He simply scheduled a lunch in Manhattan with the landlord. Since I was not a fly on the wall, I don't know what they said to each other, but Richard left the restaurant that day with a check to NORD from the landlord for several thousand dollars.

I ended up renting an office not too far from my home on the second floor of a building housing physicians' offices in New Fairfield, a small town north of Danbury. As NORD grew, we rented adjoining offices until we occupied almost the entire second floor. The landlord never asked us to discriminate against anybody. However, he did refuse to put in an elevator; the ADA, which required that all new buildings must be accessible for handicapped people, exempted old buildings like the one that NORD was initially housed in. People with mobility impairments are discriminated against whenever a building is not accessible to them, so after a decade we moved to an accessible building in Danbury.

*

After the NORD office was set up, Bill Haddad called me and asked if I remembered the meeting we had in New York about creating a computerized rare disease database. I keenly remembered the academic expert who said she could do it for $200,000 a year. Bill said he and his member companies still wanted the database, but not for $200,000. "If I give you a one-time gift of $30,000 do you think you can start the database?" he asked. I replied, "I'll try."

At that time (1986) the Internet existed, but was only in its infancy. Only universities and government agencies were allowed to use it. The only computer service company that welcomed the public was a private company called CompuServe.

I hired some nursing students who wanted part-time work to write database entries about rare diseases in understandable language. These entries were uploaded to CompuServe. We prioritized which disease entries would be written first according the number of inquiries we received about a specific disease.

Our Rare Disease Database was successful, but CompuServe simply gave the public a sample taste of what life could be like if the Internet ever became fully available to the public. The husband and wife team, we worked with at CompuServe, saw the writing on the wall, and when the Internet went public (thanks to Al Gore) we moved the Rare Disease Database to the Internet. The challenge then was to get enough revenue to update the online disease descriptions, and to write more new entries for the thousands of diseases that were not yet online. Ongoing funding for updating and expanding the Rare Disease Database became a perpetual challenge, but always a top priority for NORD.

*

I only had $30,000 for the office expenses for the first year. Then I was visited by Shirley Friedland, who used to be my boss as executive director of the Tourette Syndrome Association. We talked a lot because I always appreciated the advice she gave me, but it was obvious that I would not get through the first year unless I could find more revenue.

Shirley suggested holding an award banquet and honor some people and companies who have been important to the orphan drug effort. Fundraising banquets were one of Shirley's specialties. I felt like I had no choice. I had to take a leap of faith because the money would not come in otherwise. So Shirley Friedland started us out with a fundraising event in Washington DC, thereafter becoming an annual event. We raised about $50,000 that first year and in every year following we increased the amount over the year before. We took the opportunity to honor individuals, politicians and companies that developed important orphan drugs which represented a major advancement in treatment for serious and life threatening rare diseases.

*

I quickly learned that NORD was like any other small company. Networking and contacts would be vitally important to the company's success, especially early on. Fortunately for me, in those early days, I met several tremendous people whose generosity and goodwill were essential to NORD's success.

One of those people was Agnes Varis. Bill Haddad introduced me to Agnes whom I came to love like a favorite aunt. Agnes was the child of Greek immigrants. She grew up in Brooklyn and majored in chemistry at Brooklyn College. She also studied at the Stern School of Business at New York University. When she graduated she got a job at a chemical firm, which sold chemicals to pharmaceutical manufacturers. After 10 or more years, when the owner retired, Agnes bought the company from him. She knew everything about the business, and she had the contacts to ensure success. She married late in life and never had children, but she loved her cats as if they were her children.

When I met Agnes she was a mega-millionaire. Her company, Agvar Chemicals, sold chemicals to brand name and generic drug companies, but she was considered one of the most important figures responsible for the American generic drug industry. Her chemical company was in New Jersey, but she moved into Manhattan to a duplex condominium apartment on Central Park South. Her husband was a music lover, so the second floor of their apartment had a studio for him where he could listen to his music while viewing the most magnificent scene in the city, southern Central Park.

Agnes was on the Board of Directors of the Metropolitan Opera and several other coveted Boards of Directors. Every morning, her chauffeur drove Agnes in her Bentley to her New Jersey company, and at night he drove her back again. This continued until her husband was diagnosed with Alzheimer's disease. She eventually moved her company's administrative office to Manhattan so she could spend more time with her ailing husband.

Agnes was absolutely devoted to FDR style Democratic politics and she had little patience for Republicans (they also had little patience for her). She was one of the founders of the Generic Pharmaceutical Industry Association (GPIA), but she had no love for the Republican men who were CEOs of many of the generic drug companies. She would fall out of favor with them for being unabashedly liberal, but in the end they had to appreciate that Agnes had the contacts in Congress that they needed. She was on a first name basis with the most important Democrats in Congress and the White House.

Those most responsible for passage of the Drug Price Competition and Patent Term Restoration Act were primarily Bill Haddad, his assistant Dee Fensterer, and Agnes Varis. The law was sponsored and introduced by Senator Orin Hatch (conservative Republican of Utah) and Congressman Henry Waxman (liberal Democrat of California). The combination of these two legislators was so unusual that they were dubbed "strange bedfellows." But the legislation that they wrote became one of the most important free-market laws of the 20th century because the intense competition that it spurred in pharmaceutical pricing drove down the cost of most pharmaceuticals to 20% of the brand name price within 3 years of losing the branded drug's patent.

Several years later, when the high cost of biotechnology drugs were bankrupting families, I went to Agnes about the need for a generic biologics law. No one could simply copy a biologic treatment and put it on the market the way a chemical drug could be copied and sold as a generic drug. The only way to bring down prices of biologic medicines, which were priced at thousands of dollars per year, would be to facilitate competition from less expensive biologics. But this would require another federal law because the FDA had no legal authority at that time to approve copies of biologic treatments.

Agnes donated money for NORD to conduct a conference in Washington DC about generic biologics, and that conference started the ball rolling. Suddenly there were conferences popping up all over the United States debating the scientific question of whether generic biologics could be "bioequivalent" to brand name biologics. We issued a white paper report on the conference and about 3 years later a generic biologic provision was inserted into President Obama's health care reform law. Today we have more affordable biologic medicines that are termed "biosimilars" because of Agnes Varis.

Agnes died in 2011. She was a great friend and I miss talking to her. She held nothing back and you always got her opinion whether you wanted it or not. The thing I admired most about Agnes was her determination to make her money work for people. After Sept. 11, she donated $10 million to a charity in New York City to provide free prescription drugs to any person in New York City who had no health insurance or who lost their health insurance because of the Sept. 11 attack. After hurricane Katrina hit New Orleans, she and her husband worried obsessively that New Orleans jazz musicians would not be able to make a living. So she donated millions of dollars to a music foundation to pay salaries to displaced New Orleans musicians as long as they would perform at least once each week...anywhere. Agnes told me, "Jazz is the only music form that is quintessentially American. We have to take care of Jazz musicians or be prepared to lose that American art form." And because of her love for opera, she donated millions to the Metropolitan Opera in NYC to provide inexpensive seats to ordinary people who could not afford the opera's regular seat prices. She made the opera accessible to thousands of people who could not otherwise afford to see it.

Agnes and her husband were cremated. She did not have a memorial service for her husband or herself. There is no cemetery I can visit to pay my respects. But I will never forget her. I heard less than a year later that the most expensive apartment in New York City's history was sold on Central Park South. It was a two story apartment. I do not know if it was Agnes' apartment, but if it was, I hope it will ring with music forever.

*

One of the wonderful things that came out of the struggle to pass the Orphan Drug Act was the numerous times that help arrived from unexpected sources. Two people who greatly helped me during the early days of NORD were Max Link and Craig Burrell, who were both medical doctors working in the pharmaceutical field. Max was the CEO of the American arm of Sandoz Pharmaceuticals and Craig was the Executive Vice President of the corporation who made sure things got done the way Max wanted. Max and Craig did their utmost to introduce me to the important New Yorkers who were active in the health arena. When the Orphan Drug Act was going through Congress a man named Joel Bennett had started a foundation in NYC to raise money for research on rare diseases. Although the foundation was legally incorporated, it had not actually raised money, nor hired staff. Now that NORD was on the scene, Craig suggested that perhaps the Foundation should be merged into NORD, which meant that NORD would have to create a medical research grant program.

This probably would be a no-brainer under any other circumstances, but NORD was a coalition of rare disease charities that raised funds for research on their own diseases. They didn't want NORD competing with them. In an agonizingly slow process, I had to illustrate to our member charities that there are several thousands of rare diseases that have no charities representing them, yet families afflicted by those diseases are often eager to raise money or personally donate for research on their disease. But in the absence of a charity dedicated to their disease, there is no way for them to spur research unless NORD could do it. For most rare diseases, a lot of affected families would have to join forces and raise enough money because one small grant would cost $30,000 to $50,000 per year. But every dollar designated for research on a specific disease, would have to be reserved for that disease under the research program that NORD eventually created.

Once NORD's member organizations understood that they did not cover all rare diseases, we easily illustrated that if NORD had a research program it would be no threat to them. Eventually the Board of Directors agreed that we could start a research grant programand they consented to the merger with the foundation dedicated to rare disease research.

*

Max Link hosted a dinner meeting with some of the people who were on the Board of Directors or advisors to the research foundation. The meeting was at a high end French restaurant, Le Circe, in New York City. I felt self-conscious about wearing a J.C. Penny suit to a 5-star restaurant, but I met several people who became valuable contacts during the years ahead.

Mathilde Krim, PhD, was an active cancer researcher who was studying interferon. She was married to Arthur Krim, a New York lawyer who headed United Artists Motion Picture Company and later founded Orion Pictures. She and her husband were politically active in the Democratic Party.

Someone had gotten Mathilde's attention for a new disease starting on the west coast among gay men. She became so devoted to the AIDS/HIV movement that she started the AIDS Medical Foundation, which later merged with another AIDS group to become amfAR- the American Foundation for AIDS Research. I greatly enjoyed talking to Mathilde because in the beginning AIDS was considered to be rare enough to represent a very small potential market, but Mathilde knew that AIDS would soon become a growing epidemic that would affect millions of people all over the world. She fought a mighty battle with the Reagan administration to bring attention to AIDS along with research dollars, and Mathilde won every skirmish. I also met Alice Fordyce at the dinner meeting. Alice was Mary Lasker's sister. Mary Woodard Lasker was a health activist and philanthropist who began the Albert & Mary Lasker Foundation in 1942 to promote medical research. Alice became very involved with the Lasker Foundation after Mary's death. Every year the Foundation would award prizes to scientists who made the most important medical discoveries. It was commonplace for Lasker award winners to later win the Nobel Prize in Medicine, so even today a Lasker Foundation award remains one of the most prestigious scientific prizes in the world. Alice was a good friend of Gene Gardner, an executive at one of New York's largest banks, and she introduced him to me. Gene was a very close friend of Joel Bennett who had started the rare disease research foundation.

Also among the leaders I met that night was a research dermatologist from New York University. Since most dermatologists don't go into research, she became a valuable contact who could find out where to get dermatology questions answered for severe and life threatening skin diseases. But at the time of our dinner meeting she didn't have a clue about the meaning of "orphan drugs." "What does this term mean? Are they treatments for orphans?" she asked. "I explained the problem and the fact that Congress had passed the Orphan Drug Act. Now it was up to patient organizations, research scientists and pharmaceutical companies to work together to promote development of new treatments for diseases affecting fewer than 200,000 Americans. There were more than 6,000 of these diseases and only a handful had treatments at the time, so we needed to raise money to fund research on diseases that had been ignored for too long.

They asked for examples of some rare diseases that they might know. I explained that hemophilia affected only 10,000 males in the U.S., cystic fibrosis affected only 25,000, Duchene muscular dystrophy affected only 15,000 and Lou Gehrig's disease (ALS or amyotrophic lateral sclerosis) affected fewer than 30,000 people in the U.S. They knew the names of these diseases, but had never thought about them in terms of a potential market for a medication.

They agreed to the merger. Even though the bank account of the foundation yielded only about $5,000, which was promptly paid out in legal costs for the merger, our research program provided a home for the donations of many people who wanted to foster research on diseases affecting their loved ones. Unlike other research funds that supported "basic research," NORD's research funds were aimed at research on new treatments: drugs, medical devices, medical foods, etc. Later, this type of research became known as "translational research"; translating basic research discoveries into treatments, cures, preventives, laboratory tests and other medical products.

Unbelievably, many of NORD's research donors wanted to donate for research on rare types of cancer. I would ask them, why don't you donate your money to the American Cancer Society? ACS is a huge multi-million dollar charity that funds a lot of research. They told us the ACS would not reserve their donations for a certain type of cancer; instead the money would be spent on basic research for cancer in general. Since there are more than 200 different types of cancer, these donors did not want their hard earned money to be spent on common cancers that were already benefitting from many coordinated fund raising campaigns (e.g., breast cancer, prostate cancer, lung cancer, etc.). Instead, they wanted to be assured that the money would support research on unusual cancers such as cancer of the saliva gland, rare brain tumors, pancreatic cancer, etc. Thus the needs of NORD's members and friends dictated the programs and services that NORD created.

*

The various people discussed in this chapter were vital to the formation of NORD. Whether they were directly affected by a rare disorder or whether they simply understood the critical importance of the Orphan Drug Act, all of them played a role in bringing the rare disease community together.

The rare disease community needed to band together because the early years of the Orphan Drug Act did not start with a bang. Like a sulking child, the pharmaceutical industry dragged its feet in exploring the benefits of the law. And, like a young child on a swing, the pharmaceutical industry needed a push to get orphan drug production rolling. That push would come from unexpected sources.

Chapter 5

Baby Steps

"Never doubt that a small group of thoughtful committed citizens can change the world. Indeed, it is the only thing that ever has."

Margaret Mead

In 1982, just before the Orphan Drug Act became law, I went to a meeting at the Department of Health & Human Services, which provided a forum for the drug industry, the government and rare disease consumer organizations to talk with each other. I was a bit late to the meeting because my plane from New York arrived late. As I got off the elevator and walked to the meeting room in the Hubert Humphrey Building, I heard a man's loud voice talking with passion to representatives of the Pharmaceutical Manufacturer's Association who were probably half-way across the room.

"Why won't you voluntarily do it?" he asked. "I represent all the small generic drug companies and I can tell you right now that we will manufacture any orphan drug that can't find a sponsor, even though our companies can hardly afford to do so." This was how I first met Bill Haddad.

"You know you should do it," he continued, "and you can certainly afford to do it, SO GET OFF YOUR ASS AND DO IT!"

Bill Haddad was quite a character. He started as an investigative newspaper reporter and he lived the rest of his life as if he was about to reveal all the hidden factoids that people had tried to bury. When he was young, his investigative journalism had brought him to the attention of Senator Estes Kefauver, who was well known for his crusading investigations of corporations and industries. Haddad went to work for Kefauver and was a key figure in the anti-trust investigation of antibiotic pricing in the United States. Several pharmaceutical companies conspired to keep antibiotic prices artificially high and Kefauver's staff uncovered the conspiracy.

At a break in the proceedings of the orphan drug meeting Haddad met me in the hallway and introduced himself. I asked if he really meant what he said about generic companies willing to manufacture orphan drugs. He said 'absolutely,' but he wanted me to understand that generic companies are in the business of copying drugs that were invented elsewhere. So they don't have big research staff who know how to get a brand new compound tested and approved for marketing by the FDA. Nevertheless, they can make the drugs and ensure that each tablet is bioequivalent and if there is need for more it would have to be negotiated with each company.

Since generic companies didn't have experienced and adequately trained medical, scientific and regulatory people on staff, they would have to hire consultants to steer them through the New Drug Application (NDA) process at the FDA. It would be a lengthy and expensive process for them and I wondered if they were about to step into a morass that they would later regret. Nevertheless, we desperately needed the quick decisions that privately held companies could make because they did not have to answer to Wall Street and their stockholders were usually the family that owned the company.

I knew the first orphan drug that the generic companies should start with: L-5HTP for myoclonus. I called Dr. Van Woert who was still packing pill capsules by hand in his laboratory. He was excited to hear that there was any possibility for a machine to make his drug, instead of his recovered patients. Bill Haddad put me in touch with a small generic drug company on Long Island, named Bolar Pharmaceutical, and Dr. Van Woert and I went to visit.

The CEO of Bolar gave us a tour of his factory. Dr. Van Woert explained that his drug would have very low demand because very few people have myoclonus. The CEO showed us a machine that is made to produce very small batches of drugs, and Dr. Van Woert thought it would be appropriate. They discussed the FDA's rules about getting experimental drugs to patients, under a special arrangement called a "Compassionate Investigational New Drug" or "IND." Bolar's CEO wanted to know whether Dr. Van Woert felt it was important to get the drug approved by the FDA so it could be sold in the United States. Companies were not allowed to charge for experimental drugs under normal circumstances.

Actually, Dr. Van Woert said, he didn't think it would be possible to get it through the FDA approval process because it would be required to go through "double blind clinical trials." That means some patients would get the real drug, while others would get an inactive placebo, but neither the patients nor their physicians would know which medicines were real and which were placebos. However, L-5HTP caused severe diarrhea so both the doctor and patient would know immediately if they ingested the real drug.

Thus the manufacturer, Bolar, knew from the outset that L-5HTP would stay as an experimental drug until an improved treatment could take its place.

This arrangement was a huge relief to Dr. Van Woert because he had spent years trying to get the drug adopted by a pharmaceutical company. The arrangement worked very well until one day, a few years later, when Bolar got caught cheating on a generic drug application that they submitted to the FDA. The CEO was indicted, he went to jail, and the company was closed. Eventually another generic company bought what was left of Bolar and continued to make L-5HTP as an experimental drug that was available to patients under the Compassionate IND program.

Today other improved neurology drugs on the market are used for myoclonus treatment, so L-5HTP is no longer needed in the United States as a treatment for myoclonus. However, it is sold over-the-counter as a nutritional supplement. Supplements are not drugs. Since FDA does not regulate nutritional supplements, there is no way to tell if the compound resembles the original drug. As long as manufacturers do not make health claims on their labels or packaging about the therapeutic value of their products, nutritional supplements can be marketed for a variety of conditions (usually touted in health related magazines) without proven efficacy. But I don't envy their gastrointestinal symptoms from L-5HTP!

*

When I first met Bill Haddad, I knew very little about generic drugs or what role they could possibly play in the orphan drug movement, but I learned quickly. Bill Haddad became involved in the orphan drug movement because he knew it was the right thing to do and he hoped that he could embarrass big companies into adopting orphan drugs.

However, most big companies are not motivated by embarrassment or shame, only profit. Haddad was lobbying very hard at that time for Congressional passage of the "Drug Price Competition and Patent Term Restoration Act" which was finally enacted in 1984, and that law launched the generic drug industry in the way it exists today in the United States. However, the big pharmaceutical companies at the time of this 1982 conference knew what Haddad was up to, and they had launched an army of lobbyists to Capitol Hill in an effort to defeat any and all proposals that Haddad would make. Therefore, Bill Haddad's support of orphan drug legislation was perceived as just another weapon that Haddad was aiming at the brand name drug industry.

*

Although the pharmaceutical industry in general continued to ignore orphan drugs, generic companies did not. They continued to help, and their help was invaluable to many patients and families. The second drug that we asked the generic industry to adopt was cysteamine for treatment of cystinosis, a hereditary multisystem disorder that forms crystals in various organs of the body, especially the kidneys and eyes. Children with cystinosis usually experience kidney failure and blindness before they die in their teenage years (or before).

Dr. Jess Thoene was a researcher at the University of Michigan whose specialty was cystinosis. Dr. Thoene and his colleagues, Dr. Jerry Schneider at the University of California, San Diego and Dr. William Gahl at the National Institutes of Health (NIH), had formulated a drug called cysteamine that could dissolve the crystals. However, no company would make the drug because it had a bad smell and there were only a few hundred children with cystinosis in the United States.

Dr. Thoene knew a retired chemist and asked him if he could make the drug. The chemist converted a garage where the smell would not bother anyone and for several years cysteamine was made in the chemist's garage for the children who could not live without it.

During the late 1980s, Bill Haddad put me in touch with Milan "Mike" Puskar who owned a generic drug company called Mylan Pharmaceuticals, which was based in West Virginia. Dr. Thoene went to visit Mylan and they arranged for the company to manufacture cysteamine. Since it was the only medicine for cystinosis, families from all over the world were blessed with access to their treatment through Mylan. The German chemist who had manufactured the drug in his garage for several years was finally able to shut his garage shop down.

Eventually, Dr. Thoene and his colleagues were able to conduct the clinical studies that the FDA required for a new drug approval and in 1994 cysteamine was approved by the FDA for the American market. It is still used today under the brand name Cystagon®. Dr. Thoene became so devoted to NORD's mission that he served voluntarily as Chairman of NORD's Board of Directors for more than ten years.

*

Bill Haddad rallied the generic industry behind orphan drugs and stayed devoted to the cause through the coming decades. I once mentioned Haddad's name to a person I knew socially and he said, "Is that the same Bill Haddad who wrote the book about shared custody?" I didn't think so, but I did some research and learned that Haddad had indeed written several books, one of which was about shared custody of children from divorced parents. This made him a hero in the movement for father's rights. But to us in the area of health policy it was Bill Haddad who had a hand in writing and passing the Drug Price Competition and Patent Term Restoration

Act. The law enabled generic drugs to get to the American market as soon as the brand name drug patent expired, thereby greatly reducing health care costs to millions of Americans. Before the legislation was enacted brand name drug companies were able to delay generic copies of their expensive drugs for decades even after their patents had expired.

*

With an actual office, part time staffers and the fledgling Rare Disease Database, NORD was beginning to grow and take shape. In those early days, many people were instrumental to the continued growth and success of NORD.

It was at this time that I first met Max Link and Craig Burrell who worked for Sandoz Pharmaceuticals. Sandoz was one of the three giant international pharmaceutical companies based in Switzerland: Hoffmann-La Roche, Ciba-Geigy and Sandoz. In 1996, after Max and Craig retired, Ciba-Geigy merged with Sandoz and became "Novartis", one of the largest pharmaceutical companyies in the world today.

I first met Craig after someone told me he wanted to meet me. He was a physician who had heard about the orphan drug movement and felt it was a worthy issue. We made an appointment for lunch in a restaurant in New York City. On the way down to the city I got caught in a massive traffic jam and was mortified to meet Craig about 30 minutes late. There were no cell phones in the 1980s so there was no way to phone someone to tell them you would be late. After apologizing profusely, I told Craig I was extremely happy to meet him because several neurologists had mentioned a problem they were having with a Sandoz drug known as bromocriptine mesylate (Parlodel®). The drug was actually developed for a common health condition but it was well known that it worked on Parkinson's disease. Although Parkinson's disease is no longer a rare disorder, at one time it had been considered relatively rare because patients stayed home and would not go to see a doctor because they knew that there was no treatment for the disease. It wasn't until after the development of L-dopa that Parkinson's patients came out of the woodwork in droves because a treatment was finally available. At the time I met with Craig in the late 1980s, dopamine had been on the American market for more than a decade, so no one still believed that Parkinson's was rare. Today estimates suggest that there may be as many as one million people with Parkinson's disease in the United States.

However, on the day when I met Craig for lunch, the problem was that Parlodel worked in high doses for Parkinson's disease, but it was only sold in low dosage pills aimed at a common condition; preventing lactation in mothers who did not want to breastfeed. As a result, neurologists told me their Parkinson's patients had to take eight or 10 (or more) pills at a time, several times a day, which was very difficult for elderly disabled patients to swallow. I asked Craig if he could look into it and he did. Within a few weeks, he told me Sandoz had applied for the FDA's permission to manufacture higher dose pills. He thanked me for bringing the problem to his attention because Sandoz had no idea about this need.

Parlodel is still sometimes used to treat Parkinson's disease today. It is no longer used to prevent lactation in women who have just given birth. Sandoz stopped the sale of Parlodel for this indication in 1994 and the official labeling of Parlodel no longer mentions lactation.

Craig was a British physician who lived many years in the United States. His children were grown and some of them became physicians. He lived in New Jersey with his wife, but he always planned to retire in his birthplace, Wales. Sandoz had a large campus in New Jersey and a small office near Rockefeller Center in New York City. It was the first drug company to make organ transplants possible because it developed cyclosporine (Sandimmune®), a drug that tamps down the immune system so it would not attack and destroy a newly transplanted organ. Sandoz could have asked the FDA for an orphan drug designation when cyclosporine was developed because at the time there were very few kidney, liver or heart transplants annually in the United States. However, the company choose not to ask the FDA for an orphan drug designation because it knew the drug would become very profitable based on: 1) A very high price in comparison to other drugs on the U.S. market at that time, and 2) Even though organ transplants were rare at that time, Sandoz knew the number of transplants would increase exponentially as soon as doctors were confident that cyclosporine would greatly reduce organ rejections.

I always appreciated that Sandoz did not seek an orphan drug designation for cyclosporine because it would have violated the spirit of the original Orphan Drug Act, which defined eligible orphan pharmaceuticals according to the predicted profitability of a drug. I always appreciated Craig Burrell addressing the concerns of the patient community about Parlodel. However, the issue of Parlodel underscores the biggest problems in the early days of the Orphan Drug Act. Pharmaceutical companies were accustomed to thinking big: big patient populations would lead to big profits. They never explored the need for treatments of uncommon diseases. Orphan drugs were facing an industry whose thinking was deeply entrenched in this model.

I realized one of two things needed to happen – current pharmaceutical executives needed to change their thinking or new, innovative people willing to take risks needed to become involved. Craig eventually retired and moved to his beloved

Wales, but Max Link stayed in the United States and became involved with several small biotechnology companies that specialized in orphan drug development.

*

An example of such innovative thinking came from a neurologist at the Albert Einstein School of Medicine in the Bronx, NY. He called me one day in the mid-1980s to say he was a neurologist specializing in multiple sclerosis (MS), and he had been experimenting with a drug that appeared to be effective on MS. He had spoken to several pharmaceutical companies about this drug but they were not interested. Firstly, they told him, there weren't a lot of people with MS so the market would be too small. Secondly, most neurological diseases (especially MS) wax and wane, so it's too difficult to prove that any medication has caused an MS patient to go into remission. The remission may occur without any treatment at all.

I called the National Multiple Sclerosis Society to talk to their medical director, Stephen Reingold, PhD, to find out if the neurologist was authentic. Sylvia Lawry had retired. Steve said the doctor was a well-known MS neurologist whowas aware of the promising drug that was used in that small clinical trial. But it was not a big enough trial and it didn't last long enough to actually tell whether the drug would pan out.

I did some more investigating and found that the drug, which eventually came to be known as Copaxone®, was actually invented in Israel at the Weizmann Institute of Science. So its ownership was unclear. I phoned Dr. George Goldstein and asked if he could help me out. He worked for a large pharmaceutical company called Sterling Drug that was later bought by another large drug company. But George was active in the Pharmaceutical Manufacturer's Association (PMA) and he wanted to be helpful.

I put Dr. Goldstein in touch with the Einstein neurologist and told him what I knew about the Weizmann Institute, and he took it from there. When he got back to me a few weeks later he explained the complicated history of the drug; somehow W.R. Grace & Company, a chemical conglomerate, owned the patent on the compound, so anyone who wanted to negotiate a deal on the patent would have to communicate with W.R. Grace and the Weizmann Institute.

After that conversation I picked up the phone and called Bill Fletcher, the CEO of the North American branch of Teva Pharmaceutical Industries, LTD, which is an Israeli generic drug company. I explained the problem and gave him the phone number for the Einstein neurologist, Stephen Reingold at the MS Society, George Goldstein at Sterling Drug and told him about W.R. Grace. "Please," I said, "If there is anyone who can straighten this out it would be your company because you are an Israeli company. But I can tell you there is no treatment for MS at this time and most patients deteriorate over time. So any drug that can show even a minimal sustained improvement will be a blessing."

Teva did fix the problems in Israel, then it developed Copaxone over a period of several years. Teva had never developed a brand name drug before, so the whole process of applying to the FDA for a new drug approval was new to the company. In the end, Copaxone became a blockbuster drug selling over $1 billion a year and Teva eventually opened a brand name subsidiary company called Teva Neuroscience. Bill Fletcher retired in the 1990s. Today there are many drugs available to treat MS, but in the late 1980s there was nothing until Bill Fletcher picked up the ball and ran with it. Teva deserved to score the touchdown.

When a new treatment is developed for a rare disease, patients often come out of the closet. After three or four new orphan drugs were approved for the treatment of MS the FDA determined that MS was no longer rare. MS patients no longer stayed out of physician offices because they had no hope of treatment and there were way more than 200,000 of them in the United States. Today the FDA no longer designates treatments for MS as "orphan drugs," but people with MS all over the world are still benefiting from the original orphan drug treatments for MS that pharmaceutical companies did not want to develop without financial incentives.

*

Another barrier in the early days of the Orphan Drug Act was funding for medical research, which was always a big issue, but was a particularly thorny one when talking about rare disorders. Many politicians and ordinary people bristled at spending millions of dollars for research on rare disorders that only affected small numbers of people.

However, the medical community was quickly learning that many rare disorders potentially held answers for more common health conditions and that research into rare disorders could be beneficial to society as a whole.

Obviously, pharmaceutical companies had little interest in rare disorder research before the passage of the Orphan Drug Act, but neither did the government. However, the FDA did establish the Office for Orphan Products Development (OOPD), which is dedicated to advancing the development of treatments and medical devices for rare diseases. The Orphan Drug Act provided a funding mechanism for grants that OOPD could award to scientists, universities and companies in support of their research on new drugs, devices and medical foods. But every year I had to beg congressional appropriations committees to fund the grant program.

After Dr. Marion Finkel retired the OOPD was run by Dr. Marlene Haffner for more than 20 years. Marlene was a dedicated public servant who initially started her public service career as a physician at hospitals serving American Indian reservations. Her husband, an obstetrician and gynecologist, also worked on Indian reservations. When they moved to Washington, her husband worked at a government hospital serving the armed services, and Marlene got a job at the FDA. Soon she was put in charge of the OOPD and even after retiring she remains totally devoted to the success of the worldwide orphan drug effort.

Marlene Haffner has always been an example to me of the ideal public servant who does her job not for glory, not for riches, but to answer the needs of people who desperately need good government programs and policies. One of her responsibilities was administering the orphan products research grant program, which was a program mandated by the Orphan Drug Act. The aim of that program was to support translational research that would move good ideas from the laboratories of research scientists into clinical trials to prove that they will work on human illnesses. Marlene's office, the OOPD, was also assigned responsibility for the Humanitarian Device program when that legislation became law.

During the 1990s, to everyone's surprise, an amendment called the Humanitarian Device Exemption was added to the Safe Medical Devices Act of 1990 that was going through Congress. Hardly noticed, it passed and was signed into law. No one who cared about this legislation bothered to contact NORD and ask our opinion. Months later I learned about the law when I happened to get an airplane seat next to the lawyer who got the Humanitarian Device Exemption passed into law. He noticed I was reading something about orphan drugs so he struck up a conversation.

He explained that he worked with a medical device company who knew there was a real problem getting manufacturers to study devices for small numbers of people, simply because the FDA required large expensive clinical trials that would be impossible to conduct on rare diseases. So he got the Humanitarian Device Exemption passed so that medical devices for conditions affecting fewer than 4,000 people in the U.S. could get on the market with minimal evidence of safety and effectiveness.

I wished he had come to us before the law was enacted because together we could have written a much better law. Eventually problems arose when health insurers refused to pay for humanitarian devices because they insisted they were "experimental" since they were not proven conclusively to be safe and effective. But the FDA made several official statements convincing insurers that humanitarian devices were NOT experimental; they were approved by the FDA for sale in the United States and finally they were reimbursed by insurers.

We knew that surgeons complained the tools they had in the operating room were primarily developed for adults. The biggest problem was doing surgery on children, especially infants, with implements that were too big. Since few device companies made smaller size devices, surgeons often had to alter adult-sized gadgets or create other instruments from scratch. But it was not clear that there would be less than 4,000 such surgeries per year for any of these pediatric tools. Nevertheless, we were not given an opportunity to discuss these issues before the law was passed. I was also worried that the minimal amount of safety and efficacy evidence could enable unsafe or ineffective medical devices to eventually reach the market, but there was nothing I could do about it now.

The lawyer/lobbyist told me they chose the 4,000 population cut-off because the device company that he was working for had one device they were concerned about, and they estimated it would be used on fewer than 4,000 patients per year. This reinforced my concerns because it is surely not good public policy to design a law based on the needs of only one product and one company.

The basic problem with the Humanitarian Device Exemption is that it allows medical devices to reach the U.S. market if they are proven "safe" and "probably effective." Unfortunately, however, patients and their doctors rely on the FDA's marketing approval as a guarantee of safety AND effectiveness. Therefore, the Humanitarian Device Exemption was fated to fall under a cloud of scandal when a device to treat an advanced abdominal cancer was being used to treat other cancers "off-label" without any proof that patients would benefit and on many more than 4,000 patients.

If the attorney who wrote the law had communicated with NORD first, we would have explained to him that patients were unwilling to allow medical products on the market to treat rare diseases unless they were proven to be both "safe" AND "effective." Thus the development of any rare disease law had to address the way smaller clinical trials could prove safety and efficacy because there were not thousands of patients available for clinical trials. The Humanitarian Device Exemption law did not address this important issue – it simply said a device could reach the U.S. market if it was "probably" effective. In the years since, many patients have benefited from the law, but it also set the stage for opportunists who inflated the "effectiveness" of their devices in the quest for profit. One area in particular where these opportunists thrived was treatments for cancer.

After the Humanitarian device bill was passed the FDA's OOPD was given responsibility for the law, including deciding which devices would be designated as "Humanitarian Devices." Meanwhile, OOPD was being besieged by grant requests for orphan product research projects, without increased funding from Congress to hire extra staff who would handle the expanding workload.

The orphan product research grant program was started the year before the Orphan Drug Act became law because Congressman Jamie Whitten (D-MS) appropriated the money to start it. The grant program soon became one of the most successful government supported research programs that did not simply prove or disprove scientific theories; it resulted in new medical products that actually saved lives.

*

Congressman Jamie Whitten of Mississippi was an elderly gentleman who spoke with such a thick southern drawl it was like a foreign language to my ear. I had to watch his lips when he spoke so I could try to interpret at least some of what he was saying. He served 53 years in Congress.

Congressman Whitten was extremely powerful because in 1982, he was Chairman of the House Appropriations Committee. All the money the federal government spent annually had to go through his committee. Mr. Whitten told me he had a hard time with migraine headaches. They made his life unbearable at times and he wanted somebody—anybody—to do something about new treatments. So in the 1982 congressional appropriations report (a year before the Orphan Drug Act became law), he ordered the FDA to set up an Office for Orphan Products Development (OOPD), and gave it a half-million dollars to start a research grant program for the development of new treatments for rare diseases.

Mr. Whitten didn't know that migraine headaches are not rare so research on migraine headache medications would not qualify for the grants, but the program he created was a blessing for us. By 2011 at least 50 orphan drugs and "humanitarian medical devices" on the American market had been developed with a grant from Jamie Whitten's orphan drug grant program. Congress appropriates only about $10 million per year for the program in recent years, and every year I have to ask what miracles could have been wrought if Congress simply doubled the amount they grudgingly appropriate annually. What treatments and cures for how many diseases are ignored each year because the FDA does not have enough money to fund them?

*

Because the government's research grants for orphan product development was very limited, NORD created a research grant program that enabled people to donate and restrict their gift to a disease they named. A good example of the way NORD's research program was meant to work involved a medical device known as the Titanium Expandable Rib.

One year the OOPD received a grant application from a Texas orthopedist, Dr. Robert Campbell, who had been challenged by a very unusual case of an infant patient who was born without ribs.

When a person inhales their lungs expand but this child's chest was too small and his lungs could not sufficiently expand. If Dr. Campbell could't do anything, the child would die of asphyxiation. He tried to design a contraption that would do the job of the ribs, with the daunting problem that it had to be expandable to allow for the child's future growth. When he applied for an FDA Orphan Product grant he did not have enough evidence that such a gadget would work. It first had to be tested on several children.

In the late 1980s, someone from the OOPD office called me and asked if NORD would consider a grant application from Dr. Campbell. This person felt that the grant outlined a much needed clinical trial for a very rare medical condition that always leads to death. But most of our research money had to be restricted to the disease that people donated for, and no one had donated for an absence of ribs. However, we did get a small number of research donations that were not restricted to a specific disease, but may be restricted to pediatric diseases, bone diseases, etc. So I told the OOPD it was okay for them to refer Dr. Campbell to us, even though I could not guarantee it would be funded. Our Medical Advisory Board had to review all grant proposals and they decided what would be funded based solely on scientific merit and availability of funding.

NORD funded Dr. Campbell's research grant and he studied eight or 10 children who were born without ribs or had only partial ribs. Later he used that data to apply for a large government grant from the OOPD. This time he had enough evidence to indicate his expandable rib worked, so the FDA funded his larger clinical trial. Instead of making each device himself, Dr. Campbell got a medical device company to manufacture it and finally after several more years the titanium expandable rib was approved by FDA in 2004 as a Humanitarian Device. Today, it is used all over the world for these unique and rare birth defects.

Dr. Campbell is a gentle, wise and compassionate man. He left private practice to go into research because he was compelled by his vision to do good. Years later he gave me a photo album with pictures of the children who have been saved by his titanium rib. I treasure that album because I know it was not the rib that saved the children; it was the man.

*

Despite the initial successes brought on by the Orphan Drug Act, the law failed to address every issue it should have. And, as with any law, there are always unanticipated consequences. Most laws are living documents and often need to adapt and restructure moving forward. The Orphan Drug Act proved no different. It became apparent early on that the law would need to be amended; my days of lobbying the government were not over. We were successful in getting some of these critical amendments passed, but with others we fell short of our goal.

Unfortunately, the failure to pass one amendment in particular, an amendment that was vetoed by the first President Bush, still resounds today and may eventually threaten the very existence of the Orphan Drug Act itself at some point in the future.

Chapter 6

Amendments & Consequences

"Those who love sausage and respect the law are better off not watching either one being made."

Mark Twain

As difficult as it was to get the Orphan Drug Act through Congress, more difficult problems layed ahead. There were things missing in the law that needed to be added and other things that needed to be amended going forward. Some of these issues became apparent in the first and second year after the Orphan Drug Act became law, but it took more than a decade for the large multinational pharmaceutical companies to understand how important the law would become to their future. And the ongoing challenge in every year ahead was trying to out-guess and out-maneuver individual companies who wanted to tweak the law in ways that would benefit their drug and their company, no matter how much it might hurt individual patients and their families.

The first problem was the absence of a definition for the word "rare"; a maximum size for the rare disease population that would enable a drug to qualify for an orphan drug designation. The original law simply said that a drug for a disease that was "rare in the United States" could qualify for the benefits of the Orphan Drug Act, but the FDA said without a definition for the word "rare" they were hesitant to name any drug as an "orphan drug."

We came up with a numerical definition: a disease is rare if it affects fewer than 200,000 people in the United States. How did we arrive to that number?

The government official in charge of the FDA's Office for Orphan Products Development (OOPD) at the time was Dr. Marion Finkel, who was extremely instrumental in getting the FDA to recognize the problem of orphan drugs several years before the legislation was conceived. A committed public servant, she had Chaired two previous interdepartmental committees on "Significant Drugs of Limited Commercial Value" during the 1970s. The committees issued official reports making recommendations about what could be done to encourage companies to manufacture drugs for rare diseases. As usual these comprehensive reports were put on a shelf where they collected dust until we were seeking documents to validate the orphan drug problem.

After the Orphan Drug Act was passed, whenever there were meetings about orphan drugs, they tended to be male dominated meetings because pharmaceutical company executives were almost exclusively male. It seemed to me that they often tried to eavesdrop on Marion's conversations so they could gain an advantage on upcoming FDA policy issues. Thus, the only place Marion and I could talk privately was in the ladies room.

One day on Capitol Hill I asked Marion to join me in the ladies room and we discussed a number-based definition for the word "rare" and where the cut-off number should be. Marion favored 100,000 people in the United States and I favored 200,000. Then I named a number of diseases affecting just under 200,000 cases in the United States, for which there was no company willing to develop a treatment. I told her the names of the drugs and the diseases: we both were familiar with an experimental drug for narcolepsy and a drug for multiple sclerosis, but Marion was unaware that no drug companies were willing to manufacture those pharmaceuticals.

A medical journal had recently published a paper estimating the prevalence of narcolepsy to be around 150,000 people in the U.S., and multiple sclerosis was believed at that time to affect approximately 180,000 Americans. Years later both estimates turned out to be inaccurate (narcolepsy is now estimated to affect 100,000 people in the U.S. and MS affects much more than 180,000) but they were generally believed to be precise population estimates at that time (according to valid medical journal articles).

Tourette syndrome was also estimated by the NIH at that time as affecting 100,000 Americans, but some good natured researchers inevitably suggested in medical journal articles that the prevalence of TS was likely much higher, which gave them a basis to demand more research grant money for a more prevalent disease. But they were combining the more common and benign "passing tics of childhood", with the most severe tic disorder, Tourette syndrome. Obviously, TS is a socially crippling movement disorder whereas passing tics of childhood is a temporary benign condition that does not include involuntary noises and words. The two conditions may be genetically linked (they often occur in the same families) but they are not the same. It was easy for Marion to see that the 100,000 cut-off number that she favored would likely exclude Tourette syndrome, a disease that had a track record for being tagged as "not profitable enough," if the neurologists succeeded in their effort to combine all tic disorders into one diagnostic unit.

Because of this discussion Marion agreed to the 200,000 population cut-off that I advocated for. We also agreed that the definition should apply to "under 200,000 people in the United States" because tropical diseases may be prevalent throughout the rest of the world, but very rare in the United States. If the Orphan Drug Act would provide incentives for development of treatments for tropical diseases, that would be an additional blessing for mankind.

The second major issue was the fact that the incentives of the new law only applied to "unpatentable" drugs. A small number of orphan drugs were unpatentable, but the majority could be patented in various ways. For some their combination of ingredients could be patented or their method of manufacture or the drug's use on a specific disease ("use patent"), etc... But other manufacturers could easily get the same medicine on the market if they developed another way to manufacture the drug or if they proved to the FDA that the drug worked on another disease or if they substituted an inactive ingredient, etc.

The third major issue was that the original law applied to "drugs" or "pharmaceuticals," but not to "biologics." The FDA regulated biologics differently from drugs because drugs were composed of chemicals, whereas biologics were historically made from components of living substances such as proteins, enzymes, blood or plasma products, etc. For example, hemophilia is treated with a component of blood called factor VIII, diabetes is treated with insulin that initially was taken from pigs or cattle, and these treatments were regulated as "biologics" not "drugs."

In the beginning of the 20th century, officials at the FDA decided that drug and biologic products must be regulated by different sectors of the agency because biologics carried different dangers than chemical drugs. For example, a biologic made from human blood or animal tissues could transfer infections from the living donor to the recipient of the tissue. This separation of drugs and biologics existed until biotechnology emerged as a valid manufacturing process, in the late 1980s, after the time that the Orphan Drug Act became law. For example, instead of taking insulin from a cow or pig pancreas for injection into a human with diabetes, a company could grow a huge supply of insulin in large vats using bacteria or Chinese hamster ovary cells as mini-factories that would spit out quantities of insulin every day for many years. This manufacturing process is known as "biotechnology," and the treatments are classified as "biologics."

In 1983 when the Orphan Drug Act became law, the biotechnology industry in the U.S. was in its infancy. Two of the most well-known biotechnology companies today are Genentech and Amgen, and they were young new companies in the early 1980s. Both are located in California. One of the very first biotechnology products to be approved by the FDA was human insulin, called Humulin, from Eli Lilly and Company. It was Genentech that actually developed the product and licensed it to Eli Lilly so that Lilly could manufacture the insulin itself. The benefit for humans were a presumed lower cost for manufacturing an endless supply of human growth hormone and reduced chances for allergic reactions or antibody production against a medicine that the human body recognizes as a foreign substance derived from animals.

Biotechnology was safer and it was hoped that biologics made from the new technology would be less expensive. Additionally, there would be less harm to animals since they would not have to be sacrificed for vials of medicine.

The news that biotechnology was finally coming to fruition held the promise that soon it would be possible to manufacture adequate amounts of vital medical components such as enzymes and proteins that are necessary for human health. Most standard drug companies could not manufacture these biologic substances, such as interferon or interleukin, in large enough quantities until they were able to build separate factories and manage the new technology. But start-up biotechnology companies such as Amgen and Genentech were poised to reap the huge profits that the new technology would attain because they would be the first to set prices for biotechnology medicines.

To everyone's surprise, biotechnology engineered medicines turned out to be much more expensive than expected, especially because biotechnology was supposed to reduce manufacturing costs, not raise them. Chemical drugs, which had cost a few hundred dollars for a year of treatment, were suddenly overshadowed by biotechnology engineered drugs that cost thousands of dollars per year. Even biotechnology-manufactured insulin for diabetes saw huge price increases over the affordable prices diabetics had been paying for animal-derived insulin.

*

A group of scientists at NIH became very hopeful that perhaps the new technology could be used to manufacture human growth hormone. They had been experimenting with the hormone for over a decade on a small number of children with pituitary dwarfism; their bodies didn't manufacture enough of the hormone and, consequently, they were extremely tiny human beings who could not even reach faucets on a sink or cook on a stove. Since the researchers could not manufacture the human hormone, they were getting it from the pituitary glands of cadavers – people who died for various reasons and even unknown reasons.

The NIH doctors followed the children who had been given the hormone for many years, but even though they did grow to adequate height, it was eventually discovered that some of them were dying prematurely from a very rare condition known as

Creutzfeld-Jakob disease (CJD). CJD is a "prion" disease; prions are infectious elements that are not a virus or bacteria, but can cause extreme disability and death.

For example, variant Creutzfeld-Jakob disease (vCJD) is a prion disease that usually takes several years to develop in humans who are believed to get it from eating meat derived from cows (or deer, elk or other wild game) that ate foods contaminated with prions. In cows, the disease is known as bovine spongiform encephalopathy or "Mad Cow disease." Prion diseases such as classic or variant CJD weaken the body and mind, and are always fatal. The disease (CJD, not Mad Cow Disease) is so rare it affects only one in one million Americans, so when several cases were identified in people with dwarfism who had received human growth hormone from cadavers, scientists learned that taking growth hormone from dead humans was the source of the prions and it could no longer be allowed.

Thus, the researchers asked Genentech if the company could develop and manufacture human growth hormone through biotechnology. The company did manufacture the hormone and it planned to benefit from the orphan drug incentives. The company, however, was surprised in 1983 to learn that "biologics" did not qualify as "orphan drugs" because biologics were not mentioned in the original law.

When we realized that biologics were omitted from the law we requested that it should be amended to the law. Enzymes, proteins and the like offered the promise of treatments for thousands of genetic diseases, so biologics just had to be covered by the law. Thus the first changes to the Orphan Drug Act were the population definition (fewer than 200,000 people in the United States), the ability of "patentable" medicines to qualify for an orphan drug designation and the addition of "biologics" in the group of eligible products that could be designated as an "orphan drug." Shortly thereafter, Genentech requested and was awarded, an orphan drug designation for recombinant human growth hormone (hGH), even though the incentives of the law were not needed to attract the company into developing it. The Orphan Drug Act was almost an afterthought for Genentech, but the company quickly learned to seek orphan drug designations for any of their future products aimed at rare health conditions because it would prevent competition for 7 years during which they could charge any price they wanted for their medicine.

Sitting (left to right) Abbey Meyers and Sharon Dobkin. Standing and leaning on crutch (from a basketball injury) Senator Orin Hatch (R-UT), Rep. Henry Waxman (D-CA) and Rep. Ted Weiss (D-NY). Congressman Weiss died in 1992 from a sudden heart attack. This photo was taken around two years after the ODA became law. The press conference was held to explain Orphan Drug Act amendments that were being proposed.

Unfortunately, giving the orphan drug designation to hGH turned out to be a big problem. Firstly, the cost of the product was more than $20,000 per child, per year (depending on the weight of the child), and the cost escalated each year as the child grew up to $100,000 or more before the child could stop taking it in the late teenage years. Naturally, parents complained to their Congressmen about the price. Was it right for the company to charge so much for a treatment that it had already been developed before financial incentives contained in the law became available for biologics? In other words, Genentech invested in research and development of hGH well before the Orphan Drug Act created financial incentives to lure companies into developing biotechnology treatments for rare diseases. Additionally, much of hGH's development was paid for by the federal government through the National Institutes of Health (NIH).

Several years later, because of Genentech's late application for an orphan drug designation, which was submitted to the FDA a few days before the company received marketing approval, an amendment to the Orphan Drug Act was passed requiring companies to get their orphan drug designation at least one year BEFORE they apply for marketing approval. Thus, a signal was sent to the industry reminding them that the legislation's financial incentives are there to lure companies into developing medicines they would not ordinarily be attracted to, and not simply as a toy to prevent competition on very lucrative medicines.

Additionally, shortly after hGH got on the market body builders and athletes found out that they could grow big muscles with hGH; it quickly became an underground drug for weightlifters and athletes and it did not show up on blood tests for steroids. Some clinics advertised that hGH was an "anti-aging" medicine, and opened quasi-medical clinics promising perpetual youth.

In a short time, hGH became so profitable that several other companies went into the hGH business outside of the United States and smuggled their biologics into the country for use at gyms and underground clinics for prevention of aging. Of course wealthy sports fanatics did not know or care about the possible dangers of hGH, including the possibility of the hormone causing cancer cells to multiply.

I remember talking to a federal law enforcement authority about hGH and he told me most of the vials that agents were confiscating had labels written in a foreign language, so consumers could not be warned about dangers of hGH unless they could understand the language. Some of the vials were Genentech's own product that had been shipped to Mexico or South America and then smuggled back to the U.S. There was no evidence that Genentech did anything wrong, thus, the company was not prosecuted. Law enforcement focused on people illegally selling hGH without prescriptions and smugglers who brought hGH across the American border.

Other biotech companies soon realized that the exclusivity provided by the orphan drug law offered a 7 year market monopoly for that medicine's use only on a specific rare disease. So they developed their own biotechnology engineered hGH and got it approved for other rare diseases (not pituitary dwarfism). Soon there were five or more other brands of hGH on the U.S. market for a wide variety of rare diseases. It was apparent that the market was profitable enough for several companies to compete with their own human growth hormone. But each company was only permitted to market their hGH for the disease that the FDA approved it for.

The hormone was not used solely to treat dwarfism. It effectively treated a group of very serious handicapping conditions such as pediatric kidney diseases that delayed growth. It was also used on children who were simply short, whose affluent parents wanted them to grow taller. Insurance rarely paid for hGH unless it was used for a valid and serious health condition (not simply short children), but wealthy parents who could afford to pay $20,000 to $100,000 a year until the child turned 16 or 17. Height, especially for boys, made it a good cash investment in their child's future, these parents thought. It was unethical perhaps, but not illegal as long as a doctor prescribed it.

Some Senators and Congressmen could not help asking why the benefits of the Orphan Drug Act were granted to such a profitable drug. Wasn't the law written for "drugs of limited commercial value?" Trying to explain the perversion of the law by a small number of companies became a mental exercise of acrobatic proportions (without a safety net). I was never able to defend the behavior of those companies to congressional staff except to say that patient advocates had absolutely no influence over corporate pricing policies, nor corporate social consciences.

*

During the 1990s, hearings were held in the Senate by Senator Howard Metzenbaum (D-OH). Several families testified about the impact of astonishingly high orphan drug prices, including a woman with Gaucher disease, and the family of a boy who required hGH injections because he had no pituitary gland. It had been removed in childhood due to a brain tumor. Thus his body was unable to manufacture any natural human growth hormone. His father, a certified public accountant, had to leave his job because the cost of health insurance at his small firm increased so high that other employees could not afford their health insurance. He had to find another job at a big company, to preventthe cost of his health insurance from increasing insurance costs for the rest of the employees.

The family moved away and the father got a menial job at a large factory, in order to get health insurance that covered human growth hormone without driving up premium prices for other employees. The only other alternative would have been to divorce his wife and drive the family into poverty so the boy could get Medicaid benefits. Unfortunately, many families with very sick children (e.g., cystic fibrosis, hemophilia, etc.) had to choose this option when there were no alternatives for uninsured American families.

After Sen. Metzenbaum held initial Senate hearings on rare disease drug pricing, the House of Representatives joined the chorus for reform because they learned some orphan drugs were discovered and developed at least partially with federal funds. They asked how companies could charge $100,000 to $300,000 per year or more for a drug that was developed with tax payer money. As with hGh, they asked, "Weren't orphan drugs supposed to be "drugs of limited commercial value?"

During the administration of the first President George Bush, an amendment was created by Rep. Henry Waxman and Sen. Metzenbaum, allowing the U.S. government to review the sales of an orphan drug after its fifth year on the market and, if it had become a drug of substantial commercial value, the government could cut short the company's remaining exclusive marketing rights. This would enable the FDA to approve generic copies of the drug. Competition from generic drugs was, and still is, the only thing that brings drug prices down in the United States.

With great difficulty the amendment passed the House and the Senate, but then President Bush vetoed the bill and it never became law.

Genentech never reduced its price for human growth hormone and the government could do nothing about it. **In the American "free**

market" system our government does not control prices.
But Europe, Canada, Japan and many other industrialized countries
do control the prices of medicines, those consumers have always
paid less than Americans for all pharmaceuticals, not just orphan
drugs. It did not take very long for me to realize that American
consumers are subsidizing the reduced prices of drugs that the rest
of the world benefits from.

In time the cost of hGH looked like a bargain in comparison with
the cost of other biotechnology engineered drugs. Today, in the U.S.,
the orphan drug Soliris costs over $400,000 per year to treat two
rare diseases: one is called paroxysmal nocturnal hemoglobinuria
(PNH) and the other is atypical hemolytic uremic syndrome. The net
sales for Soliris in 2012 were just over $1 billion and the company is
exploring other potential indications for that drug. Another orphan
drug, Elaprase, which treats Hunter syndrome, costs $375,000 per
year; Myozyme, for Pompe disease, costs $300,000 per year; and
Cerezyme for Gaucher disease costs $200,000 to $400,000 per year
depending on the weight of the patient.

*

Although the pricing of rare disease drugs continued to be a major
problem, without orphan drug incentives, many biologic orphan
drugs would not have been developed without the Orphan Drug Act.
The most notable of these was Ceredase (now known as Cerezyme),
because it opened the door to enzyme replacement treatments for
several serious and rare genetic disorders.

Gaucher disease is a life-threatening genetic disease that is caused
by a shortage or absence of the enzyme glucocerebrosidase. It
primarily affects people of east European Jewish heritage and French
Canadians with Acadian heritage. The disease causes crippling
bone pain, a greatly swollen spleen, broken bones and agonizing

death. Some people with the gene will never get sick, while others will suffer incredibly and die. Some people begin to have symptoms as children, but the majority experience symptoms in adulthood. If you have the genetic defect, there is no way to predict who will get symptoms and who won't.

Dr. Roscoe Brady, a devoted research scientist at the NIH, discovered that if he could replace the missing enzyme in symptomatic Gaucher disease patients, they could live a normal life. The problem was where to get enough of the enzyme.

Dr. Brady found the enzyme was a component of the human placenta, which is usually discarded after a woman gives birth. He asked local hospitals with maternity wards to save placental tissue for him. By boiling down many placentas he was able to get enough enzyme to treat a small number of children, but it was a long tiresome process that he could not continue even though there were many Gaucher patients who desperately needed the treatment.

So NIH issued a contract for a company to supply the enzyme and two chemists at Tufts University just outside Boston won the contract. They were able to furnish Dr. Brady with enough enzyme to treat more patients. Those chemists formed a corporation and named it Genzyme, which eventually became a powerhouse biotechnology company in Boston. Genzyme knew that in France there was a factory that used a large quantity of placentas collected from Africa to make lanolin, primarily used for skin creams. They arranged with that factory to get the enzyme needed for the Gaucher's disease biologic.

Ceredase was approved by the FDA in 1991 based on a tiny clinical trial of 12 patients, showing that the drug shrunk their oversized livers and spleens, and their anemia improved. As usual, as soon as the treatment became available, patients came out of the closet. But even today only about 5,000 Gaucher patients in the world (including about 2,000 in the U.S.) are taking enzyme replacement therapy.

However, when Ceredase came on the U.S. market it was the most expensive drug in the world. A number of patients with mild disease decided not to take it because they did not want to drive their family into poverty. A child treated with Ceredase could be treated for about $200,000 per year, but a full grown adult male could cost $400,000 or more per year. Dosage is generally based on body weight.

In Europe, some national health authorities said they would not pay for the treatment unless the patient was so sick he or she was expected to die soon. In the U.S., Genzyme hired a lot of staff to educate insurance companies and government health authorities about the need to pay for the treatment in order to avoid human suffering. Obviously each country, or each insurance company, would have very few Gaucher disease patients because the disease was so rare, so the overall cost to the country, or the insurance company, would generally be minimal (e.g., a tiny fraction of the amount spent overall on antibiotics or cholesterol medicines).

I learned later that the FDA urged Genzyme to develop technology that would produce the enzyme through biotechnology instead of using human placentas. The agency was concerned that the placentas from Africa might contain viruses, including the HIV virus, since AIDS was growing prevalent in Africa and the tissue was probably collected under unsanitary conditions. But while Genzyme developed technology to manufacture the enzyme, the company also had to build a new factory where the technology could be used.

Thus Genzyme developed Cerezyme; the biotechnology manufactured enzyme that did not use human placentas. Cerezyme (imiglucerase) was approved by the FDA in 1994 based on a comparison of 15 patients on the human placenta-derived enzyme and 15 patients on the biotechnology-derived enzyme. In terms of costs for this research, a study involving only 30 patients was certainly not as expensive as clinical trials for common diseases which involve thousands of patients.

Genzyme had a lobbyist who I came to know very well. Lisa Raines was a lawyer who initially worked for the trade group, Biotechnology Industry Organization (BIO). When Genzyme's CEO, Henri Termeer, asked her to work for the company, Lisa made the transition easily. I was a real pain in the neck to Genzyme during those years because a lot of reporters would call me, and when they asked, "Which is the most expensive orphan drug?" I always replied that it was Ceredase. Thus Genzyme was getting publicity it didn't want and Lisa always defended the price by explaining that it took dozens and dozens of placentas to treat one patient. "That's why it's so expensive," she would tell them.

Lisa would also say that Genzyme had to charge such a high price because it was developing technology to manufacture large quantities of the enzyme without using placentas. I could understand that because it would be safer for patients and, once the enzyme was made in huge vats through biotechnology, the price would surely drop. So when I received a phone call one day from Lisa, and I knew from Wall Street reports that the biotech version of the enzyme was almost ready for FDA approval, I expected she wanted to tell me that the new version of the enzyme was approved by the FDA. She did share the good news with me, but then she said "You'll have to thank me because I convinced Henri (Genzyme's CEO) not to raise the price on the new product, which will be called Cerezyme. It will be the exact same price as Ceredase."

Poor Lisa could have heard my reaction without a telephone from my Connecticut office to hers in Washington, D.C. I could not believe what I heard. The whole point of biotechnology was to enable manufacturing of large quantities of biologics at a much lower cost than collecting large quantities from human or animal tissues.

I have to say that poor Roscoe Brady, the distinguished elderly NIH physician who invented treatments for several life-threatening enzyme deficiency diseases, got the brunt of Genzyme's pricing practices, even though he had no influence over anything the company did. But Dr. Brady saw and listened to the patients and he listened to other doctors treating Gaucher families. Everyone lamented the cost of Genzyme's product, but it kept people alive. Inevitably, before ObamaCare many patients lost everything they owned and had to go on Medicaid (the American medical insurance system for people in poverty), because they could not afford a drug that costs as much as buying a new house every year for the rest of their life.

Eventually Genzyme was bought by the European drug company, Sanofi. One or two other companies now have competing enzyme replacement products on the market for Gaucher disease (e.g., Shire), which gives patients a choice. Generic competition usually brings prices down substantially, but generic biologics have not been on the market long enough to tell what their long term influence will be. Unlike generic chemical drugs, manufacturers of "biosimilar" biologics are required to perform clinical trials, which will drive up the cost of their medicines.

I liked Lisa Raines very much. She was a formidable foe and we both enjoyed an intelligent argument. I knew in the end that we would likely agree on a compromise and serenity would return for a while. I also knew that what Genzyme did was prove to the rest of the industry that you can earn big profits on an orphan drug, no matter how small the market size is. After Cerezyme, other enzyme replacement therapies came to market for diseases even more rare than Gaucher disease, and they were also priced very high.

In time I realized it was not so much the price of the drug that caused human misery, it was the fault of the American health care system. Even if we could afford health insurance, there was no guarantee that an insurance company would sell us a policy if we had a pre-existing condition. We needed mandatory, universal health insurance so no one would be denied the medicines they need to stay alive. **The government and insurance companies should be arguing with drug manufacturers about prices, NOT the patients!**

Photo was taken at a public event in Washington DC sometime between 1992 to 1995 when Hillary Clinton was trying to pass national health insurance legislation. Her enemies named it "HillaryCare" and succeeded in killing the legislation. I am standing 2 rows behind Hillary on a stepped platform.

On September 12 or 13, 2001 I received a phone call from a *NY Times* reporter, asking me about Lisa Raines. I began to answer but then wondered why he was asking. After all, shouldn't he be calling Genzyme, not me?

"Why are you asking?" I said. "Haven't you heard?" he replied, "Lisa was on the plane that flew into the Pentagon on September 11."

It was like a punch in the stomach. I needed several minutes to get my breath back. "I'll tell you one thing," I said. "Lisa would not have simply sat there. She would have told them exactly what she thought of them and tried to argue them into submission. She would have fought back with her last ounce of strength."

*

The veto by the first President Bush of the Waxman-Metzenbaum amendment to the Orphan Drug Act opened the door for pharmaceutical companies to exploit the provisions of the law enabling them to create blockbuster drugs with huge profits – never the intended purpose of the law.

The irony of the pharmaceutical industry furiously lobbying the President to preserve a law that they had vehemently opposed only several years earlier was not lost on me. Unfortunately, their lobbying, buoyed by their deep pockets, was successful and the pricing of orphan drugs would steadily grow into a huge problem, one that exists to this day and still requires an equitable solution.

Chapter 7

Stemming the Tide

"Be who you are and say what you feel, because those who mind don't matter, and those who matter don't mind."

Dr. Seuss, author of childhood books.

The problem of paying for extraordinarily expensive orphan drugs became more serious as time went on, primarily because the American health insurance problem became worse and worse over time. The cost of all drugs (not just orphan drugs) continued to escalate which put drug prices in a position of political controversy. NORD began to sense that a solution was needed before droves of rare disease patients would be denied treatments they could not afford.

NORD became committed to ensuring that patients had access to life saving medications and, eventually, NORD would create a Medication Assistance Program (which we called "MAP"). MAP was designed to provide life sustaining drugs (or biologics) to needy people in the United States who did not have health insurance, and could not afford to purchase the treatments themselves. Every year the number of uninsured Americans was rising and once someone had a "pre-existing condition," insurers refused to sell that person health insurance regardless of how much you could pay for monthly premiums. I first learned about this problem when I tried to get health insurance for David after he graduated from high school, but a decade later the problem became far worse because insurers were refusing to sell health policies to people with common benign health conditions like asthma, hypertension, etc., that were treatable with common medications.

Initially, MAP enabled uninsured, needy rare disease patients to obtain free orphan drugs until they could either purchase health insurance (usually when their spouse changed jobs and the new employer offered a different policy), or qualify for a government insurance program such as Medicare or Medicaid. Years later, the program was expanded to include payment of health insurance premiums for needy patients, payments for copays or deductibles and "expanded Access Programs" that enabled patients to have access to certain experimental orphan drugs if they could not get into a sanctioned clinical trial.

People who needed one of the drugs in our MAP programs were told to complete an application and return it to us with proof of their monthly income and monthly expenditures. They told us how many dependents they had and what their assets were. In most cases they were people who had worked for many years and became disabled due to their medical condition. Once they became disabled, they lost their job and with it, their health insurance. When we saw what their monthly revenues were, we subtracted their monthly living expenses and could see how much, if any, revenues were left over for purchase of their monthly medicines.

When we started the MAP program we met with a group of volunteers in New York City who helped us review all cases on their merits. After a while things were moving ahead smoothly enough to bring only the most difficult cases to the volunteer panel. Once the New York panel disbanded we convened, a panel of community volunteers who came to our office once or twice each month to review the most difficult cases, until after a few years our staff was able to handle even the most unusual requests.

It certainly was an educational process for us because the great majority of applicants qualified for free drugs and a small number could afford to pay partially for the quarterly (3 month) supply of their drug. In other words, for some drugs a person would receive a 3 month supply of the drug for free, while a person who could afford to partially pay for their drug might get 8 weeks of drug for free while they were expected to purchase and pay for the remaining 4 weeks of medication from their local pharmacy. Every year they had to reapply to the NORD program so we could keep track of their progress.

As time went on, the health insurance problem worsened as the policies instituted higher co-pays and deductibles that many needy people could not afford. And then there were those who enjoyed health insurance through a spouse's employer, but when the spouse lost his/her job they could not afford to pay for their insurance policy under the government's COBRA program (A law, incidentally, that was written by Sen. Nancy Kassebaum before she retired from the Senate). We went back to the companies that were generously giving us free drug for indigent patients and asked them to donate cash that we could use to pay for co-pays, deductibles and even COBRA health insurance policies. Some companies agreed to do this and some refused.

When a pharmaceutical company donated free drugs to NORD we never received or handled the actual drugs. We made arrangements with mail order pharmacies that had appropriately licensed staff, and they received the product shipments. Then we told them who to mail the drugs to, how many pills or vials each patient was to receive for free, and they shipped the drug directly to the patient's home in appropriate packaging. Some drugs had to be refrigerated, so they were shipped overnight in special bags that contained refrigerated gel packs.

Each year a drug company would tell us how much of a drug they would donate to the MAP program. If they allotted 1,000 bottles or 10,000 bottles, we knew that we could only give away that amount and not one pill or vial more. We had to carefully budget the supply in order to help the maximum number of people. If a person could pay for $1/4$ of their dosage, that meant we could give that medicine to another person. When we reached the maximum number of free drugs distributed in a budgeted year we were forced to create a waiting list and all the people who we could not help were relegated to the waiting list until the manufacturer budgeted more drugs to the NORD program.

Sometimes a NORD staff person would tell me how upset he or she was that we couldn't help every family that needed our assistance. I could only respond that we would never have enough resources to help all of the people who merited our help, but we should certainly be grateful to the companies who enabled us to help people who would certainly die if they could not obtain the treatments. But sometimes we would come across an applicant who would make us question values that conflicted with the good deeds we were trying to perform.

- There was the man from southern California who applied for a free transplant drug. He reported his income, but under expenditures he reported $800 per month for his automobile loan. We asked him what kind of car he was driving and it was an expensive race car, like a Maserati. We turned down his request because the cost of his car loan would have paid for his monthly medicine, so we suggested he might want to sell the car. The drug we could save by not approving this patient would be given to another person who had absolutely no other way to pay for his drug.

- A nun applied for a free transplant drug. Since she was technically an employee of the church, the church was responsible for her health insurance. But the previous year, the business people of her local parish changed their insurance plan. To save money they opted for a new policy that paid for doctor's fees and hospitals but dropped all coverage for pharmaceuticals. They knew that the nun had a kidney transplant 5 years before, and would need to take transplant drugs for the rest of her life, but they took a chance that a charity would help her. Since the church was the "financially responsible party" under our rules, we asked for their IRS forms showing what their revenues were in the previous year. We gasped to see it was several million dollars, so it seemed hypocritical to try to save money by cutting back on health care for nuns and priests. We had several staff meetings to discuss this case because we felt it should be a community decision, rather than an individual decision. We decided to deny the nun's request because her church parish was responsible for her well-being and since they cancelled their initial health insurance policy they should pay cash for the drug.

- There were many other cases that elicited animated discussions and staff persons would often approach the debate reflecting their personal biases. One time, I received a call from a Senate staff person who wanted to know why we denied an application from one of the Senator's constituents. I told the staff person that I can't tell him anything about the reason we denied him free drug, but the program was designed to help indigent people who have no other resources. "And if you ask this person what kind of car he is driving he'll tell you he is driving a brand new Cadillac." I told him, "It is our judgment that if he can afford a new Cadillac he can afford his drugs. What do you think?" I asked. He simply said, "Thank you. Now I understand."

• And then there was the application from an elderly man who lived in Kentucky's horse country. His wife submitted the application and explained that this was the second marriage for both of them. While the wife owned a horse farm and had substantial revenues, she explained that they had signed a pre-nuptial agreement stipulating if either one of them got sick, each one was financially responsible for their own medical expenses. In other words, the wife did not want to pay for her husband's medical care and therefore applied to NORD for free drugs. It was our judgment, however, that no matter what they each had signed under current law the legal spouse of a sick person is responsible for the medical costs of their mate. We denied their request.

While these cases raised questions about values and responsibilities, the great majority of applicants to NORD's MAP programs were extremely needy and qualified for free drugs without question. As long as drug was available to us, people continued to get them for free until their circumstances changed. Every so often, we would get a letter or phone call from someone who thanked us for all the help we had given them, but now they said they had gotten health insurance or qualified for Medicare or Medicaid or their spouse got a new job with employer based health insurance. "Now," they told us, "you can give my drug away to another person who needs it." It was these people who truly understood what charities try to do every day of their existence.

*

Ironically, the drug that kicked off MAP was not an orphan drug. In 1987, the drug that got the ball rolling was called cyclosporine (Sandimmune®).

One day in the late 1980s, Dr. Craig Burrell of Sandoz called me because the company was under extreme pressure over the price of Sandimmune, their immune-suppressant drug used for kidney transplant patients. Sandoz was besieged by bad publicity because cyclosporine was tagged as "the most expensive drug in the world" at that time. Cyclosporine was NOT a designated orphan drug, but on an annual basis it cost about $8,000 to treat a kidney transplant patient for one year with Sandimmune. No one had any idea about the escalating price for transplant drugs in the future, but we sensed that costs would inflate upward, not down. In comparison prices for some orphan drugs eventually numbered in the hundreds of thousands of dollars annually. In retrospect now, cyclosporine was a bargain and was the first pharmaceutical that made organ transplants successful.

The idea of organ transplantation was not new. Doctors had tried transplantation for more than a decade before cyclosporine was invented, but the patient's body would ordinarily reject the new organ because the immune system recognized it as "foreign." Then Sandoz developed cyclosporine which tamed the immune system so the body would not recognize the new organ as a "foreign" entity. Even though some people continued to reject transplanted organs despite the medicine, a large percentage of people were finally able to live for an extended period of time with their new kidney, as long as they continued to take cyclosporine every day of their life. There were no other transplant drugs competing with cyclosporine at that time, and there were very few organ transplants performed annually in the United States. Today, however, there are many other medications to tamp down the immune systems of organ transplant recipients, and over a million organ and tissue transplants are done world-wide every year.

Craig explained that patients were complaining, doctors were complaining, insurers and hospitals were complaining, so Sandoz's staff was discussing how to ethically handle the problem of access by patients who could not afford the drug. Craig said that the marketing department which was responsible for sales of the transplant drug had been handling the problem on an individualized case basis, but requests for free drug were becoming overwhelming. When someone complained about the cost of Sandimmune, the company would send them a few bottles of the drug for free through their doctor's office. Inevitably, they would call back when the bottles were empty, asking for more free medicine. Could the company continue to supply free drugs to everyone who asked for it? If the company denied the drug to people who could not afford it, would they be blamed for causing needless rejections of transplanted organs and ultimately needless deaths? This was a uniquely American problem because the United States had the most advanced medical technologies but did not have national health insurance.

Like a never ending circle, the success of cyclosporine increased the demand for organ transplants, particularly kidney transplants and the success of kidney transplants increased demand for more cyclosporine. Since people have two kidneys, it became possible for a relative to donate one of their kidneys to a sibling or parent. But an increase in demand for liver, lung and heart transplants, to name a few, was not easily solved because donors had to be dead (cadavers).

Years later, doctors discovered that liver transplants from a living related donor could be successful when a portion of a donor's liver was transplanted into a person whose liver had failed.

Transplant surgeons warned that the shortage of organs reemphasized the need for patients to stay on their immune-suppressant medication religiously. If the new organ failed, the patient would likely die before another organ became available. Lists of patients waiting for a transplanted organ became longer and longer, and the demand for cyclosporine grew with each successful transplant.

The majority of organ transplants involved kidneys and many kidney patients were on dialysis. Dialysis was extremely expensive and many hoped that Sandimmune would lead to more transplants and ultimately fewer people on dialysis.

Dialysis machines were invented during WW II by a Dutch physician, Dr. Willem Kolff. The idea of cleansing toxins from the blood of animals whose kidneys stopped functioning (hemodialysis) was first tried in animals by Dr. John Abel at Johns Hopkins University in Baltimore. He published a paper about his experiment in 1913, and years later Dr. Kolff read that scientific paper. During WWII in Europe, mechanical and medical supplies were in short supply, but Dr. Kolff was determined to build a dialysis machine using cellophane tubing (artificial sausage skin), orange juice cans and a washing machine. He completed the task in 1943 and tried it in 16 patients suffering from kidney failure. All of them died.

But Dr. Kolff did not give up. Still working with his crude invention he tried it on a 67 year old woman in 1945, who came out of a uremic coma after 11 hours of dialysis. When the war was over, he donated five of his machines to hospitals around the world, including Mt. Sinai Hospital in New York City. In the late 1940s, Dr. Kolff came to the United States to train other doctors on the use of his dialysis machine. He stayed in the United States and went on to invent the heart-lung machine and an artificial heart.

Doctors learned that patients with kidney failure could live a long time if they could get dialysis several times each week to clear out the toxins that were normally disposed of by healthy kidneys. Incrementally, dialysis machines were improved, and during the 1960s the first outpatient dialysis centers were created in the United States. But dialysis was expensive, and there were not enough dialysis machines available for all of the patients who needed them. So dialysis treatments were rationed, giving preference to the youngest and healthiest patients who were most likely to benefit from the treatment, and those who could pay.

When enough machines finally became available, treatments were so expensive that few people could afford dialysis. Then a Senator's mother was diagnosed with end stage renal disease (ESRD), and he was so appalled that dialysis was rationed and expensive that he pushed for change. Congress eventually passed the *Social Security's Amendment of 1972*. One of the provisions of this Act was establishing the Medicare National End Stage Renal Disease (ESRD) Program. The only Americans who were eligible for Medicare at that time were people over 65 years of age, and disabled people who could not work for 2 or more years. When Congress enacted the ESRD Medicare program for kidney patients who needed dialysis, Medicare benefits became available to kidney patients of all ages, with no annual income requirements, no need to stop working and become permanently disabled. Rich and poor were treated alike. But dialysis could not be used forever. There was a great need to find other plausible treatments, which led to experiments with kidney transplantation.

All other patients with chronic or life-threatening diseases had to wait 2 full years after they became disabled and stopped work, in order to get Medicare benefits. This often meant that they had no medical insurance at the most critical time in their life when medical services were most needed. Thus there was major resentment that an exception to the federal Medicare rule was made only for kidney patients, and only because a politician's mother had kidney disease. When patient groups lobbied to get early Medicare benefits for other diseases, they were told not to mention the ESRD program on Capitol Hill because it was costing the government so much money there was entrenched opposition to allowing anyone else to become prematurely eligible for Medicare benefits.

It took many years before some cancer patients would be given disability and Medicare benefits before the mandatory 2 year wait. Ultimately, AIDS patients would also be given early benefits. When certain types of cancer were exempted from the waiting period, ALS (amyotrophic lateral sclerosis, also known as "Lou Gehrig Disease") patients made a huge political fuss and that disorder was ultimately exempted from the mandatory 2 year waiting period as well. Thus, one disease at a time, patients became indignant at the omission of their disease from early Medicare benefits, and reached out to politicians to solve the problem.

When cyclosporine enabled kidney transplants to actually work, Medicare faced another major problem. The ESRD program was created to cover dialysis treatments, not kidney transplants. However, publicity about the success of kidney transplantation indicated it would be so successful that patients would no longer need dialysis (which would save the federal government a lot of money) and they would be so healthy they could return to work and stop receiving disability benefits. Politicians saw dollar signs dancing in their eyes and approved payment for kidney transplant surgeries, along with one year of pharmaceutical coverage for cyclosporine.

This was all wonderful news for kidney patients, and transplants greatly multiplied. However, most of the patients who no longer needed dialysis treatments several times each week, did not get healthy enough to return to work. Many had several diagnoses aside from ESRD, such as diabetes, loss of limbs, blindness, mobility impairments and other severe illnesses. So after one year, with a new kidney functioning as smoothly as a new engine in a luxury automobile, they lost reimbursement benefits for all pharmaceuticals including cyclosporine, which was absolutely essential for retaining their new kidney. They could not work, meaning they could not pay for private insurance; even if they won the lottery and had millions of dollars, no insurance company would sell them a health insurance policy because of their "pre-existing condition."

Several years later, after substantial political uproar, Congress realized it made a mistake limiting prescription drug coverage for transplant patients to one year, they lengthened the benefit to three years of coverage. It remained at 3 years until the George W. Bush administration created the Medicare Part D program. Thus payment for cyclosporine and other competing transplant drugs was somewhat liberalized as long as a patient could get through the Part D "Donut Hole" (a period of time when drug payments stopped until the patients' expenses reached a catastrophic level). Once they paid several thousands of dollars out-of-pocket during the "donut hole" period, their pharmaceutical coverage for 95% of drug costs would resume for the rest of the year. The cycle started over again every January.

At least the kidney transplant patients had an alternative; they could go back on dialysis to stay alive awhile longer, and hope that a new kidney would become available to them soon. But there was no magic machine to keep liver and heart transplant patients alive if they rejected the new organ.

*

When Craig Burrell initially called me about the cyclosporine problem in the mid-1980s, the employees of Sandoz realized what a terrible problem these patients faced, knowing that the company would probably be blamed for the deaths that would surely occur without cyclosporine. When Craig phoned me that day he asked if I could figure out how to help the kidney transplant patients who could not pay for their cyclosporine. Obviously, a program had to be created to judge whether or not a person could afford the drug, then a system of distributing free drug to them had to be created. Craig said, "Figure out a way for NORD to do this for us because the decisions about who should get the drug should not be made by my company." Craig was a very wise man.

I knew I needed help to develop and oversee such a program as MAP. When I went to work for the Tourette Syndrome Association, I had to vacate my volunteer position as the leader of the Connecticut TSA chapter. I asked a young mother of two, Maria Hardin, to take on leadership of the chapter when I left. Maria was a special education teacher for severely handicapped children. Her daughter had TS, making her knowledgeable about what needed to be done for Connecticut TS families.

When I started the NORD office in Connecticut, I contacted Maria and asked if she would work with me at NORD, initially part-time, because I did not have enough time to provide services to all the families who contacted us. When Craig asked me to design a program that would help organ transplant patients, Maria and I contacted charities that gave items or money away to needy people, and we studied the strengths and weaknesses of those programs in order to be able to avoid making the same mistakes.

We wrote a report and plan for Craig, and Sandoz approved it. Thus NORD's Medication Assistance Program was created. NORD's Medication Assistance Program for Sandoz lasted for 10 years and taught us a lot. Many of the patients stayed in the program for years because they never recovered enough to return to work. Over time, Sandoz added other drugs to the program such as Neoral (an updated form of cyclosporine), Sandoglobulin (an intravenous immune globulin), Sandostatin (for carcinoid syndrome), Clozaril (for schizophrenia) and Parlodel (for Parkinson's disease). It was not long before other manufacturers asked us to administer similar MAP programs for their drugs. The programs grew from prescription products like cyclosporine that were approved by the FDA for sale in the United States, to experimental drugs that were not yet approved by the FDA for marketing in the United States. These were mostly cancer drugs; when news about them was leaked to the press, large numbers of people were begging companies for the drug because all other treatments had failed. The FDA had to approve each experimental drug program before we were allowed to launch them. In some cases, demand for an experimental drug outweighed the available supply so we developed a "random selection" process; instead of putting all the names in a hat and pulling out names of winners who could get the drug, the names were put into a computer and the computer randomly selected the names of people who could get the drug. As more of the drug came available, more names would be selected by the computer.

Under NORD's MAP we also developed programs for drugs in short supply, when they had to be rationed because there was not enough of the medicine for everyone who wanted it. This occurred, for example, with Botox when the company was moving the manufacturing plant from one building to another. There was a delay in the FDA approval of the new factory, so for several weeks all requests for the drug had to come through NORD to ensure it would be used only for certain serious health conditions, not cosmetic uses.

At that time Botox was approved as a treatment for certain forms of dystonia; a group of rare muscular diseases characterized by extreme painful muscle spasms.

*

During that time, another drug that was perpetually in short supply was Acthar Gel, an old biologic that was historically made from pituitary glands of pigs, for treatment of "infantile spasms" (also known as West syndrome). Infantile spasms is a severe seizure disorder in infants that causes brain damage, mental retardation and death. The drug was also used for the blindness caused by multiple sclerosis and several other diseases that were haphazardly listed on its label.

As the history of Acthar Gel was explained to us, it was originally manufactured by Armor, the meat company. At the beginning of the 1900s, a lot of drugs were derived from animals (e.g., insulin) so it was inevitable that meat packing companies went into the medicine business. Over the years, meat companies sold their medicines to pharmaceutical companies. When we became involved with Acthar Gel it was owned by a French pharmaceutical company, Rhone-Poulenc Rohrer (RPR). The company inherited the product by acquiring other companies, it was hardly conscious of Acthar Gel which sold for $40 a vial at that time. We heard that Acthar Gel was not on the company's radar screen because annual sales of the drug were miniscule; less than $1 million annually.

The FDA had obviously not looked at the manufacturing process of Acthar Gel for a very long time, and when a government inspector saw the primitive manufacturing process involving animal tissue he stopped production of the drug immediately. When pediatric neurologists realized that there was a shortage of Acthar Gel they contacted NORD and asked us to get involved. The FDA is very secretive about its decisions and does not tell the public why they have taken certain actions. So we investigated the problem and tried to understand why the stoppage occurred.

I decided to go down to the FDAs headquarters in Rockville, Maryland to tell the FDA and the manufacturer how important Acthar Gel was. RPR simply could not stop manufacturing the drug because they didn't want to spend money on upgrading their technology. For the time being, the FDA had to allow the pig-based drug to continue because pediatric neurologists had no alternative for infantile spasms. I found out when the company had scheduled a meeting with the FDA and made sure to show up at that meeting.

When I walked into the room many of the FDA staff recognized me, and said, "Excuse me, but this is a private meeting between the agency and the company, and the public is not allowed in." I replied, "Yes I know that, but I need to say something before you start this meeting, and then I'll go. I need to tell you that Acthar Gel is an extraordinarily important drug and we get calls every day from pediatric neurologists who can't get the drug because of the shortage. They tell us that babies are becoming brain damaged and some are dying because they can't get Acthar Gel. Then the adult neurologists call because they can't get the drug for their multiple sclerosis patients who have lost their eyesight. Some people are blaming the company and others are blaming the FDA. The only reason I'm here is to tell you that you cannot leave this meeting without some kind of compromise that will allow Acthar Gel to be manufactured again. You cannot allow this shortage to continue. You must find a compromise before you leave this room, because if you don't, I will let the *New York Times* and *60 Minutes* know that both the company and the FDA are responsible for the deaths of these babies."

I walked out of the room and flew home praying that they heard what I said and took me seriously, because if they failed to come to an agreement the only option left would make both the FDA and the company look terrible in the public's eye.

The following day I received a phone call from the company. The FDA agreed that they could continue manufacturing the drug under the FDA's supervision, and each lot of the drug would have to be individually approved by the FDA before it would be released to the public. But as part of the agreement, the FDA wanted a closely controlled distribution system which would be managed by NORD. No one asked if we would distribute Acthar Gel, they simply told us to do it!

All requests for the drug would have to go through NORD. We would decide who would get the drug and who wouldn't, based on the seriousness of the disease to be treated. For example, multiple sclerosis was included on the labeling of Acthar Gel, so MS patients needing the drug to reverse their blindness would be eligible to obtain the drug, but people with MS who had normal eyesight or people with other diagnoses would not be eligible.

I was surprised by the FDA's decision because we never planned on getting stuck with administration of the Acthar Gel program. But we were getting used to these surprises because several years earlier I had awoken to a *NY Times* article announcing that a federal judge in the mid-West had settled a lawsuit by a group of patients against a large pharmaceutical company. The patients had been harmed by a drug that the company manufactured. The judge created a compensation fund for discounts on future prescriptions and other remedies (e.g., free drugs for a period of time) and announced that

NORD would run the program. No one asked us if we would do this either, nor did they warn us that it was about to happen; I simply read about it in the paper!

By this point Maria had developed a large staff that was capable of adapting quickly to the demands of new programs, new patient populations and new issues. When we began getting calls for Acthar Gel we found that it was being used for 38 different diagnoses, but the company was not aware of this. However, we could not limit the use of Acthar Gel only to the labeled indications (e.g., the diagnoses listed on the drug's label under "uses"), because the biggest use, "infantile spasms" or "West syndrome," was not on the label! None of the companies that owned the drug over the past century had bothered to get it approved for that disease.

We were able to limit the use of Acthar Gel to the most serious diagnoses and got through many months of the shortage until the shortage was eased. Then a few months later, something happened to cause another shortage and we had to manage Acthar Gel again. The pattern was replicated several more times over several years until RPR finally sold the drug to a new little company called Questcor Pharmaceuticals. At that point Acthar Gel was out of our hands and NORD no longer distributed the drug.

Questcor must have promised the FDA to update the manufacturing process, because the price of a vial of Acthar Gel rose immediately from $40 per vial to $2,000. Although we heard many complaints from doctors and parents about the price rise, we sensed it was needed to bring the manufacturing technology out of the 19th century and to avoid further shortages. But a few years later we learned that the price rose again, this time from $2,000 per vial to $23,000 for a vial. This was beyond comprehension and way beyond acceptability. But NORD was powerless to do anything about it. By 2013 Acthar Gel cost $28,000 per vial and annual revenues for the drug amounted to a half-billion dollars each year. How much profit is too much profit? Unfortunately, some people think there should be no limit.

As my schoolyard friends used to say, "Well—you win some and you lose some." Somehow I think we lost the battle over Acthar Gel, except to say that we saved a lot of lives for those we were able to help. But the overall battle to make sure everyone who needed the drug would get it, even if they were unable to pay, I'm not sure the new company followed the same rules. I wish the team from RPR had continued to keep Acthar Gel because they had a conscience and they cared about patients. And the "cold hearted bureaucrats" from the FDA had the biggest heart of all because they could have forbidden RPR from manufacturing Acthar Gel from the moment their inspector walked into the factory. Thankfully, they reached a compromise before they left that conference room, knowing that many lives depended on their decision.

*

Over the years, I would sometimes talk to pharmaceutical company executives and suggest that they create medication assistance programs so that uninsured patients would be able to obtain the company's drugs. "I'm sorry," they would say, "I don't run a charity. I cannot give our products away for free."

But of course I did run a charity… NORD. And it's not an easy thing to do because I could not order a sales force to go out and sell more widgets so we can buy better computers or hold a company picnic. In general we had to rely on the goodness of others to donate the funds and the treatments that were desperately needed. And we relied on the CEOs of pharmaceutical companies to understand the inequalities of the American health care system and give us enough of their life saving drugs to help desperate and needy uninsured patients to survive.

Some CEOs understood the need and some just didn't get it. They insisted that no one is denied health care if they went to their local hospital emergency clinic. But if the patient needed a continuous supply of the drug, their emergency clinic would not provide free pills every day for the rest of their life. And hospitals would hire collection agencies to hound patients who did not pay their hospital bills, ultimately putting liens on the patient's house or car. No, health care was not free in the U.S., and neither life nor liberty nor pursuit of happiness meant a hill of beans without guaranteed universal health care.

*

Although some people working in the orphan drug world frustrated me, a strong counterbalance came from the innumerable patients and family members that dedicated their energy to improving the lives of people with rare diseases. One of those inspiring people was Priscilla Ciccariello.

I first met Priscilla after her children had grown up and had families of their own. She was a sweet loving grandmotherly woman who made you feel as if she was hugging you with kindly words.

Priscilla had raised her seven sons on Long Island. Then one of them died suddenly. An autopsy revealed that his aorta had burst (aortic dissection) and he had died immediately. A doctor noticed that he had been a tall thin man with unusually large hands and a concave deformity of his chest, and he suspected that he may have had Marfan syndrome. The aortic dissection proved conclusively that the young man did indeed have the rare hereditary disorder.

Marfan syndrome is a genetic disease of the connective tissue, which is the material between cells of the body that gives tissues form and strength. Connective tissue is found all over the body and multiple organ systems may be affected. People with the disease are often very tall and the connective tissue of their skin and internal organs is often weakened and thinned due to the overgrowth of their bodies. The specific symptoms of Marfan syndrome can vary greatly from one person to another, but the most serious potential complication involves the aorta, the main artery of the heart. If it is not diagnosed early, the tissue of the aorta eventually stretches so thin that it bursts, causing immediate death. Because both men and women with Marfan syndrome are tall, lanky and healthy looking, they are often chosen to participate in sports during their school years. When I hear about a young, tall, healthy person dying very suddenly on a basketball or tennis court, the first question in my mind is whether the child was evaluated for Marfan syndrome before he or she was invited to participate in the team sport.

The diagnosis of Priscilla's dead son triggered medical evaluations for the rest of her family (six more sons). Her husband and two more of her sons were subsequently diagnosed, and her husband died shortly thereafter. Priscilla's life had been radically transformed from a busy housewife and mother to a stunned and grieving victim of a mysterious disease that no one knew about, and no doctor knew how to fix! So she started the National Marfan Foundation to cultivate researchers, provide support services to families, and educate the public so that Marfan syndrome would get diagnosed and treated earlier, preventing unnecessary deaths.

Eventually, doctors discovered ways to repair or replace aortas that were stretched too thin in these otherwise healthy people. Her two other sons who had been diagnosed with Marfan syndrome were still alive in 2014, but one of their children (Priscilla's grandchild) died of Marfan syndrome. Her other grandchildren are well.

Priscilla's major contribution to the field of rare disease support groups comes not merely from rising above her own personal suffering, but her ability to clearly see what can be accomplished when communities that represent different, but similar disorders work together. When I had realized I could not accomplish very much working to solve the effects of Tourette syndrome on my family, I joined with other rare disease groups to create a larger constituency demanding change. Similarly, Priscilla put together a coalition of support groups for genetic diseases of connective tissue, and together the "Coalition of Heritable Disorders of Connective Tissue" was able to get the attention of elected officials, the National Institutes of Health (NIH) and academic researchers.

Today treatment for Marfan syndrome is more immediate and aggressive. No one sits around waiting for their aorta to tear, and tall lanky athletes are generally evaluated by knowledgeable doctors for any sign of connective tissue disease. And Priscilla Ciccariello is still a grandmotherly pleasant individual who cares about other people, and knows she started an effort that will live on for many years to come.

*

Although some people in the pharmaceutical industry frustrated me, there were many wonderful people and CEOs within the pharmaceutical industry who understood the unique problems of the orphan disease world and sincerely wanted to help improve people's lives. However, others did not. The success of the law was attracting companies that had no real interest in orphan drugs beyond potential profits. In some cases, the transgression of these companies wasn't simply their resistance to help or show compassion, but was their willful exploitation of the Orphan Drug Act.

When my frustration came to a boil, I reminded myself of people like Priscilla. If she had the strength to overcome her grief, to help other grieving families, certainly I could do the same. It was tireless advocates like her who inspired me to keep the welfare of patients at the highest priority, and somehow translate those needs to the pharmaceutical personnel who were overly focused on their own careers and their own bank accounts.

Chapter 8

Questionable Intentions

"Even if you're on the right track, you'll get run over if you just sit there."

Will Rogers, American Humorist

The intent of the Orphan Drug Act was to provide financial incentives to pharmaceutical companies to encourage research and development of drugs of "limited commercial value." However, the defeat of Senator Metzenbaum's amendment opened the door for the Orphan Drug Act to become a vehicle for blockbuster drugs and massive profits.

Not every company attaches exorbitant prices to their orphan drugs, but enough do that it has become a perpetual problem. These companies may not be breaking the letter of the law, but they've certainly tarnished the spirit of the law. As of the start of 2015, American insurance companies were still paying these high prices, families are still finding ways to make due, and many pharmaceutical companies are still giving away expensive drugs to the many people who can't afford their treatments. Yet there will, someday, be a breaking point, especially since the United States has finally taken the first steps toward universal health insurance coverage (commonly known as "ObamaCare").

Historically, the pharmaceutical industry has been one of the most profitable industries in America, aside from the oil industry, so there has always been a rumbling resentment about high drug prices. As the cost of American health insurance rose dramatically in the 1990s and 2000s, consumers began to look at the components of healthcare and do whatever it took to hold down medical inflation.

Most insured American patients had to cover a "co-pay" expense whenever they bought a prescription drug at their pharmacy. The rising cost of pharmaceuticals became one of the most important items implicated in health insurance inflation, because patients could feel every price hike when they picked up a prescription at their local pharmacy. Insurance companies began raising their co-pays for prescription drugs from $5 or $10 for a low cost generic drug, to $25, $35, $50, $85 or more for the more expensive brand name drugs; some patients had to pay a percentage of the retail cost of the prescription (e.g., if the retail cost was $300 the patient paying 20% of the cost would pay $60 and the patient paying 50% would pay $150). Conversely, people did not notice the rising prices for hospital rooms, surgery, etc. because those costs were generally hidden from consumers by health insurers.

When the internet became available to the general public, some American consumers began to buy their drugs from Canadian mail order pharmacies at substantially lower prices. For example, if their health insurance required them to pay 10% or 20% of the cost for a prescription drug, it was painful for them to see their co-pay rise from $10 or $20 one month for a pharmaceutical, to $60 or $80 or more a few months later.

American law regarding individuals importing drugs for their personal use was generally foggy. You could not import a drug that was not approved by the FDA for treatment of your disease, but if the FDA approved the drug for sales in the United States there was no prohibition regarding personal importation if you traveled to the foreign country, had a legal prescription for the drug and personally brought the drug back across the border for your personal use (NOT resale).

You were not allowed to have someone else bring the drug back if that person was not the person for whom the prescription was written. That is why Adam Seligman's Pimozide was confiscated by U.S. Customs officials; the drug was not approved for sale in the U.S. and the person bringing the drug across the border was a friend and not the individual for whom the prescription was written.

In general, brand name pharmaceutical companies feared that Americans would use this loophole to violate drug company patents and profits, and they lobbied to close the loophole and stop Canadian pharmacies from selling mail order drugs to Americans.

Personal importation became a major political issue during the AIDS epidemic because AIDS activists were determined to bring down the prices of treatments for HIV infection. Wanting to avoid political confrontation with AIDS activists, the federal government tended to look the other way when needy AIDS patients bought their drugs at greatly reduced prices from foreign suppliers. Knowing this, elderly people asked, if the government was allowing AIDS patients to import their drugs at lower prices, how can the government stop needy elderly Medicare patients from doing the same thing? At that time, Medicare did not pay for prescription drugs, meaning elderly patients had to pay the entire cost of their prescription drugs. The political arguments festered until Congress passed the Medicare Part D law in 2006, which finally covered prescription drugs for

Medicare beneficiaries. Nevertheless, the law contained certain gaps which caused people using expensive medications to experience at least part of the year without any pharmaceutical payment benefits.

*

Sometimes a company misjudges the environment. Instead of sticking its toe in the water to judge the temperature, it just jumps right in. After hearing so many good things about the orphan drug market, looking at all the financial incentives contained in the law and watching the meteoric rise on Wall Street of biotechnology companies that specialized in orphan drugs like Amgen, Genzyme, Genentech, Celgene and others, a company may fail to adequately survey the political environment to see whether storms are brewing. In the early 1990s, despite President Bush's veto, a huge storm was gathering over pharmaceutical pricing in general, and orphan drug pricing in particular.

The public did not realize there was a difference between pharmaceuticals for common health conditions and orphan drugs for rare disorders. Prescription drug inflation is usually noticed by adding a few cents for a prescription to treat a common health condition such as high blood pressure pills, cholesterol drugs, antibiotics and other common medicines that are sold to millions of people, not orphan drugs that are sold to small numbers of people. No health insurance company was covering hundreds of thousands of people with a rare disease, making the overall cost of treating people with rare diseases was tiny in comparison to the cost of treating millions of people with common ailments such as hypertension or depression. Nevertheless, newspapers continued to write articles about high priced orphan drugs, while TV shows made embarrassing comparisons between the price of a common drug in the U.S., compared to the price of the same drug in Canada or France.

Small new pharmaceutical companies, however, ignored growing negative public opinion when they priced their newest rare disease medicines because the companies were usually fueled by venture capitalists who wanted quick and large profits. In some cases they bought the rights to old drugs that were on the market for many years and hiked up the price of the drug to unimaginable levels. One of these companies was KV Pharmaceutical, which manufactured Makena, an orphan drug to prevent the birth of premature babies (less than 37 weeks gestation). The history of this drug was extraordinary.

In 2003, a scientific paper was published in the New England Journal of Medicine about a federally funded clinical trial of a drug identified as 17P, which reduced the risk of pre-term birth in women who had previously given birth to premature babies. In 2006, a company named Adeza Biomedical gave the brand name Gestiva to 17P, and applied for an orphan drug designation. The designation was granted in January 2007, the company applied for FDA approval of the drug that year. While the application was still pending at the FDA, Adeza Biomedical was sold to Cytyc, Inc. That company was later acquired by Hologic, Inc. Shortly thereafter KV Pharmaceuticals bought the drug from Hologic for $82 million, subject to FDA approval for marketing Gestiva in the United States.

In 2009, the FDA denied approval of the drug because the company had submitted evidence of safety and effectiveness from only one clinical trial. Hologic required KV Pharmaceuticals to pay $70 million of the price by 2010, and that raised the total price paid by KV for the drug to $200 million. The FDA allowed KV to change the name of the drug to "Makena" in 2010. In February 2011, the drug finally earned FDA approval for sale in the United States.

When Makena reached the American market the company announced its price would be $1,500 per dose. But for the initial clinical trial each dose had cost only $15. A full course of treatment from KV would now cost $29,000 because the women would need several doses. About 139,000 women were expected to need the drug each year to prevent pre-term births. The doctors who needed Makena for their patients knew they could buy the drug from a "compounding pharmacy" for only $300 per dose, refusing to buy commercial Makena at the inflated price from KV Pharmaceuticals.

When the FDA approved Makena, KV Pharmaceutical notified compounding pharmacies that they could no longer compound the drug (make it individually for a named patient) because KV had 7 years of exclusive marketing rights for the product. Compounding pharmacies are allowed to make drugs by hand when they receive a prescription from a doctor for a specific patient. They are not supposed to make batches of drugs in advance just in case patients may need it. The compounders ignored the warning from KV Pharmaceutical and continued to manufacture the 17P drug.

Because the compounded version of the drug sold for a substantially lower price, doctors advised their patients to order the drug from compounding pharmacies. But in the summer of 2012, when a compounding pharmacy in Massachusetts sold another medicine (which was contaminated) for injection into patients' spines, criticism of the drug compounding industry became the subject of major news stories. As a result of the contaminated injectable spinal drug, hundreds were sickened and dozens of people died from meningitis. Many of the other patients, who were lucky to not contract meningitis, later developed internal cysts that were painful and dangerous.

The FDA had long wanted to regulate compounding pharmacies but the compounders had lobbied very effectively in the 1990s to prevent federal regulation of the industry. As a result, the FDA had no legal authority to regulate compounding pharmacies and prevent them from supplying lower cost compounded versions of brand name drugs to doctors and hospitals, unless a significant safety problem (such as meningitis) arises from the drug. Technically, these companies were "pharmacies," not pharmaceutical "manufacturers," so they were not required to live up to federal manufacturing standards. State governments had responsibility to inspect and regulate pharmacies, but few states had enough resources and scientifically trained employees to inspect all pharmacies in their state.

The compounders refused to stop manufacturing the Makena substitute, 17P, forcing the company to ask the FDA to intervene. The FDA responded that it had no legal authority to stop the compounders as long as the doses were safe and were compounded individually for named patients. KV Pharmaceutical proceeded to sue the FDA insisting that the agency should enforce the company's 7 years of orphan drug exclusivity. The FDA refused to do so. The compounded medicine was being made years before Makena came to market and the FDA had no regulatory authority over the compounding industry. The agency tested samples of the compounded 17P medicine and in June 2012, reported that they were safe for human use.

In August 2012, KV Pharmaceutical filed for chapter 11 bankruptcy. It should have tested the waters before jumping in. Then during the fall of 2012, news about the contaminated spinal drug that was killing people because it was made in a filthy compounding pharmacy gave KV Pharmaceutical new hope that hospitals and patients would recognize the importance of FDA regulated pharmaceutical manufacturers. Still, the FDA said it could not intervene until Congress changed the law to provide the agency with authority to regulate compounding pharmacies. The FDA noted it was empowered to interfere with the Massachusetts compounding pharmacy only because people had died from the contaminated drug that was injected into their spines to relieve back pain, but no one had yet died from the compounded version of Makena "17P."

Nevertheless, a rising fear of unregulated compounding pharmacies made some doctors think twice about forgoing an FDA regulated drug manufacturer, and KV Pharmaceutical began to receive orders for their manufactured drug, Makena.

In September of 2013, KV Pharmaceutical exited bankruptcy and was still selling Makena. The price of its stock at the end of 2013 was less than 10 cents, but the company did register a profit for the 2012 calendar year. In early 2014, a federal appeals court overturned the ruling against the company and ordered a lower court judge to reconsider the lawsuit against the FDA. In May of 2014, after an ownership change, KV Pharmaceutical was rebranded as Lumara Health. Lumara Health is a private company that is not on the stock market.

*

By 2012, the most expensive orphan drug on the U.S. market cost $440,000 per year. The price was equivalent to buying two new houses a year in the mid-western United States, every year for the rest of your life. The orphan drug, Soliris®, is made by a small Connecticut company named Alexion.

Soliris is approved for a very rare disease, paroxysmal nocturnal hemoglobinuria (PNH). PNH is a life-threatening bone marrow disorder usually diagnosed in the 4th or 5th decade of life. After Soliris was on the market, the company studied and achieved an additional FDA approval of the drug for treatment of atypical hemolytic uremic syndrome (AHUS), a life threatening disease most often occurring in children between the ages of 6 months and 4 years. AHUS is a complex disorder that normally affects children and can potentially affect multiple organs of the body, especially the kidneys.

Alexion has also studied use of their drug for a very rare neurological syndrome, neuromyelitis optica, which inflames the spinal cord and eye nerves, leading to paralysis, blindness and death. Each of these diagnoses affects only a few hundred cases in the U.S., not thousands of occurrences in any one country. In June of 2014, the FDA granted an orphan drug designation for Soliris for the treatment of patients with myasthenia gravis, another rare muscle disorder.

The company says since Soliris is the only product that Alexion has on the market, the only way it could earn enough money to finance studies on these other rare diseases was to charge a very high price for the drug. Otherwise, it could not have earned enough to finance the studies that the FDA requires for additional drug approvals. However, critics warned it is only a matter of time before we see the first million dollar price tag on an orphan drug and how long can the healthcare system afford to pay these prices?

*

In the fall of 2012, a small European company obtained the first European Union marketing approval for gene therapy against familial lipoprotein lipase deficiency, a rare genetic disorder caused by deficiency of the enzyme lipoprotein lipase. Patients affected by this disorder can develop a variety of symptoms including increased levels of triglycerides in the plasma, premature atherosclerosis (heart disease), an enlarged liver or spleen, skin lesions known as xanthomas, recurrent episodes of severe pancreatitis and death.

The orphan drug gene therapy, known as Glybera®, was approved by the European drug regulatory authority, known as the European Medicines Agency or EMA, for sale in all European Union countries. The cost was announced to be between $1,200,000 and $1,600,000. But the company says it is a "cure" and no further medical treatment will be needed for the children who receive this gene therapy treatment. However, no patient treated with this therapy has lived long enough to know whether they may eventually need further treatments or not. I am anxious to hear whether national reimbursement authorities in European countries will agree to pay for this gene therapy treatment, or whether they will advise doctors to instead prescribe the older, less effective treatments which are less expensive. Will some regulatory bureaucrat calculate the number of antibiotic pills or polio vaccines that could be bought with $1,200,000? And will they decide the money would be better spent serving the health care needs of thousands of healthy children, rather than one child with a very rare disease? We can only wait and see how society will wrestle with such ethical questions.

About a year after Glybera was approved for sale in Europe, I asked a friend in London whether any reimbursement authority in an EU country has agreed to pay for the drug. "No", she said. "No country has agreed to pay until the company shows them long-term clinical data: How long do these patients live? How long have they been monitored to show that they won't need additional treatments?"

In the summer of 2015, after UniQure applied to the FDA for permission to sell their gene therapy product in the U.S., the FDA asked UniQure to perform another clinical trial (in addition to a trial that was already planned for 2016). The agency said that an additional trial was required to support a filing of a Biologics License Application (BLA). This unexpected request represented a much more difficult road to marketing approval in the U.S. than the company expected. UniQure said it was "assessing its options for pursuing regulatory approval in the U.S. going forward." The FDA remained determined not to compromise its standards for safety and effectiveness of this gene therapy product for the American market.

*

The incentives provided by the Orphan Drug Act are so appealing that some companies have attempted to gain an orphan drug designation for drugs that didn't truly meet the criteria of an orphan drug. The FDA usually denies orphan drug designations to several companies every year. Nevertheless, they continue to apply for designations that hardly stand a chance of achieving the agency's approval.

One of the most interesting orphan drugs in the history of orphan drug development is Amgen's "EPO".

Amgen was created in 1980 as one of the first companies dedicated to "biotechnology." One of its first products was a synthetic version of erythropoietin called epoetin alfa (Epogen®), better known as "EPO." EPO is a naturally occurring hormone in humans that stimulates production of red blood cells. People with kidney disease who required hemodialysis every week usually become anemic and just taking iron to treat the anemia does not always solve the problem. So Amgen used biotechnology to manufacture enough erythropoietin to treat all kidney dialysis patients who would need it. At the time, there were about 75,000 Americans on hemodialysis and not all of them would need EPO, hence the market was not very large. Until EPO was created, the standard treatment for patients whose anemia did not respond to iron pills was blood transfusions, an expensive process carrying its own risks.

In the United States, kidney dialysis patients qualify almost immediately for Medicare. Thus Medicare could easily count the number of American patients who were undergoing hemodialysis several times each week and how many of them needed blood transfusions, at what cost? Even before EPO was approved for marketing by the FDA, one of the founders of Amgen, Dr. George Rathman, negotiated with Medicare for a price the government would pay for EPO after it reached the market. Thus when the FDA approved EPO, and people began to complain about its high price, Amgen defended itself by saying the price was negotiated with the federal government even before the drug got on the market. Besides, the use of EPO in dialysis patients greatly reduced the need for blood transfusions in the kidney dialysis population. The money the government was saving from the discontinued transfusions was substantial and made EPO's price irrelevant, the company said.

Today Amgen manufactures many different biotechnology treatments in addition to Epogen such as Enbrel (etanercept) for psoriasis and rheumatoid arthritis, another blood boosting drug called Aranesp (darbepoetin alfa), Neulasta (pegfilgrastim) and Neupogen (granulocyte colony stimulating factor), which all boost growth of specific red or white blood cells. But when EPO was its only product, there was a lawsuit between Amgen and another company that challenged EPO's exclusivity and its patents.

The lawsuit caused many headlines which precipitated questions from politicians that I could not answer. "Why," they asked, "are two rich and powerful pharmaceutical companies fighting over a drug of 'limited commercial value' aimed at a small population of people?" The answer, of course, was it would become a drug of substantial commercial value because it would be used by many people with other diseases, including cancer patients who became anemic from chemotherapy and inevitably athletes and body-builders who wanted energy boosting substances that would not show up on blood and urine tests. But none of this was clear to people outside of the company when EPO initially came to market.

Here I decided to risk a working relationship with Amgen because I feared a prolonged legal battle would focus the attention of Congress on the enormous profits of some orphan drugs, and that could lead to detrimental changes in the law. I called George Rathman and asked him to compromise and settle the lawsuit for the sake of stopping the garish headlines, which tended to blame the Orphan Drug Act for protecting drugs of substantial commercial value. If he kept the lawsuit going, I knew politicians would blame the Orphan Drug Act for sheltering obscenely profitable drugs and would try to change the law. Changes would weaken the incentives of the law and risk all of the progress made thus far.

Rathman was enraged that I asked him to do this and we never spoke again. He kept the lawsuit going and the headlines continued until Amgen won the suit. By then Senator Metzenbaum had already held hearings and had called for the amendment to stop exclusive marketing rights prematurely when an orphan drug is shown to become a drug of substantial commercial value. He was especially incensed that most of EPO's sales were paid for by the federal government through Medicare and Medicaid.

George Rathman died in 2012. Amgen brags on its website that it produced the biotech industry's "first blockbuster medicine." It does not mention that it was EPO, an orphan drug that was supposed to be a drug of "limited commercial value" and used by a small number of people.

In a March 2007 congressional hearing, it was revealed that many oncologists were personally profiting from sale of high doses of EPO or Aranesp to their cancer patients. Doctors who prescribed EPO for anemia resulting from chemotherapy charged insurers and Medicare/Medicaid for the sale of the drug and administering it directly to patients and some were awarded honorariums and education grants from Amgen. Doctors were not told that EPO was causing strokes, blood clots and heart attacks, and it could multiply cancer cells in the patients who the oncologists were treating to obliterate their cancer. ("Blood Medicine: Blowing the Whistle on One of the Deadliest Prescription Drugs Ever" (PLUME 2011) by Kathleen Sharp).

In 2012, the famous cyclist Lance Armstrong gave back seven of his Tour De France titles and medals because his teammates confessed that they (and Lance) had doped their blood with hormones that were hard to trace, such as EPO and human growth hormone: BOTH are orphan drugs.

In December 2012, Amgen pled guilty to marketing its drugs for uses not approved by the FDA, most notably its anemia drugs Aranesp and EPO. Much of the case was revealed through "whistleblower lawsuits" by ex-Amgen employees who documented what Amgen had done. For example, one employee revealed that Amgen had been overfilling its vials of anemia drugs as a way of providing doctors with extra free medicine that they could charge to Medicare or insurance companies, thus increasing their revenues. The U.S. Attorney's office in Brooklyn, New York said it was investigating Amgen since 2007. Amgen paid $1 billion in federal fines and more to the employees who were fired when they refused to comply with company rules that they believed were illegal.

*

When I think about Amgen, I am always reminded of Patty Delaney who worked in the FDA's Office of Special Health Issues. I first met Patty when she was working on breast cancer issues in Washington. When she went to work at the FDA, I was ecstatic because finally a real representative of patient's needs would be behind the scenes exerting influence.

Quite suddenly Patty's husband came down with cancer. I forget which type of cancer he had, but their lives were in turmoil due to chemotherapy. Then her husband complained about dental problems and a dentist explained that his jaw bone was deteriorating. Patty searched adverse events reports and found other cases of cancer patients with deteriorating jaw bones. She suggested that some of the drugs her husband was taking for his cancer might possibly be causing deterioration of the jaw bone. She was right, even though manufacturers had never brought the problem to the FDA's attention; some drugs had to be relabeled to warn of this serious side effect.

But her husband was getting weaker and weaker. His oncologist gave him EPO or Aranesp for anemia. Patty was responsible for paying household bills during her husband's illness and she noticed he was being charged for EPO. She asked her husband if he knew he was getting EPO and he said no, he didn't know the names of drugs they were infusing into him at his chemotherapy appointments. She did a little research on EPO's adverse events and learned that there was a major controversy in the medical community over whether high dose EPO may make it easier for cancer cells to grow and spread. Some doctors believed that cancer patients should never be given "erythropoietin stimulating factors" because it's not worth treating anemia with something that makes cancer cells grow.

By the time Patty learned this it was too late for her husband. He quickly went downhill and passed away. But knowing so many other cancer patients were getting EPO or Aranesp, Patty thought the FDA should get the word out. But anytime something was written in the medical literature or popular news media about the dangers of EPO type drugs, Amgen unleashed a counter attack on the brave souls who had spoken up. Patty didn't print anything; she just talked to people, many of whom had cancer. Consequently, it wasn't long before people at Amgen learned what Patty was saying. She was told by a senior executive of Amgen that he would advise the FDA Commissioner to fire her. That was a direct threat, which only made Patty talk to more people about the dangers of EPO for cancer patients. But anytime an FDA official suggested that perhaps experts should look at this problem and perhaps a warning should be put on the drug's label, Amgen came down hard on those employees of the agency.

It was only a year or two after her husband died that Patty came down with cancer. Since she previously had cancer (that is why Patty became a patient advocate), she always suspected she would get it again and was prepared for more chemotherapy. Before the side effects would make her bedridden, she hung a sign on her hospital door: "NO EPO." But she died a few months later, leaving a teenage son without amother or father.

Nevertheless, Patty Delaney doesn't die in my world of orphan diseases. She showed me that patient advocates are not only in the nonprofit world. Sometimes they are in places you would hardly expect, such as the government, and even inside the FDA where they take their mission to protect and enhance public health very, very seriously. Every person afflicted with a serious and life threatening disease deserves a patient advocate like Patty Delaney on their side. Moreover, people inside the government who speak up for consumers should not have a heavy price to pay for speaking their conscience.

*

I learned a lot from Patty Delaney and, no matter what I do in life, no matter where I travel, I am always trying to learn something new. Even in my most relaxing moments, I have a crossword puzzle nearby because I'm hoping to learn a new word or learn proper spelling of a word I have habitually misspelled. Even when I am fully involved with a task at hand, I am often distracted by questions tangentially related. Once I go off on that tangent, there is no way to predict whether I will ever get back to the initial subject that launched new questions. This is why, when I received an unexpected invitation to spend a week at Cold Spring Harbor at its Banbury Center, I was awed.

Cold Spring Harbor is on the north shore of Long Island on a pleasant cove that is teeming with sea life and vegetation. At the end of the 19th century, a few scientists felt that the shoreline of Cold Spring Harbor on the Long Island Sound would be the perfect place to study generations of shell fish and vegetation in order to understand patterns of inheritance and Darwin's theories. Today, the laboratory has become known as a leader in biomedical research and is world renowned for its molecular biology and genetics.

Unfortunately, the Cold Spring Harbor Laboratory has a dark period in its history. In this pristine cove, dedicated to scientific advancements, a misguided theory of racial superiority and hatred were conceived and brought in one of the most despicable eras of mankind's inhumanity to man. That theory was known as "Eugenics."

The Cold Spring Harbor Laboratory was created in 1890, by the Brooklyn Institute of Arts and Sciences for the training of biology teachers who could use it to study nature at its source. Slowly over the years it solicited and received support from prominent scientists and industrialists such as Thomas Edison and Henry Ford.

In 1898 Charles Davenport, Director of Evolutionary Biology at Harvard, was named as Director of the Laboratory. Meanwhile in 1900, the genetic experiments of Gregor Mendel were rediscovered and publicized, 35 years after Mendel's Laws had been initially proposed and ignored by the scientific community. Davenport named the prominent eugenicist, Harry H. Laughlin, as his assistant at the Cold Spring Laboratory. Together, Davenport and Laughlin, refined the theories of Eugenics, which claimed that certain races were superior to others.

Davenport asked the Carnegie Institute in Washington for support to establish a genetic research institute at Cold Spring Harbor. In 1904, the Carnegie Institute established its "Station for Experimental Evolution" on the property. In 1921, the station was re-named the Carnegie Institution Department of Genetics. Because of the support from the Carnegie Institution, prominent scientists and industrialists, the misguided theories of eugenics took hold on the American public. This led to enactment of federal laws aimed at preventing large numbers of "racially inferior" people (mostly from southern and eastern Europe) from immigrating to the United States. Meanwhile immigration rules were eased for immigrants from the Nordic counties, Germany and Great Britain.

Fortunately, by the 1930s, the American public began to reject the overtly biased unscientific theories of Eugenics because other scientists were proving such theories were false. Most Americans simply could not reject their neighbors and friends based on the size of their skull, the shape of their eyes or nose or the geographic area of their forefathers' births. Unfortunately, however, the theory of eugenics took firm hold in Germany and Austria, and with the rise of Hitler, eugenics theories were adopted with a passion in certain countries where discrimination against minorities was acceptable. The result was the slaughter of Jews, Gypsies, mentally retarded people, homosexuals and others, all based on entirely bogus "scientific" theories of eugenics. In 1935, the Carnegie Institution began to investigate the scientific basis of the theories, and in 1939, the institute withdrew its funding entirely, leading to the closure of the eugenics office at Cold Spring Harbor.

When I received the invitation to attend a one week course immersing myself in scientific and bioethics knowledge, I wondered why I was selected since Banbury Center is invitation-only, and they are limited to a small number of people at any one time. I finally learned that the invitees were people such as health reporters, writers, leaders of disease charities, teachers and hospital administrators who all had the capacity to teach others what they learned at Cold Spring Harbor. All of us were in positions to educate others about science and ethics in research.

I absorbed everything I learned at the lectures, from early morning to late at night. Much of it was new to me, especially the shameful role that Cold Spring Harbor played in the Eugenics movement. But I had heard about some horrific medical experiments such as the

Tuskegee experiment. The study involved young needy black males (mainly sharecroppers) who lived in southern states, the study was performed without the participants' "informed consent." In other words the men did not give their permission and had no idea that they were in a scientific study. The majority of the men had syphilis but the scientists did not inform them that they had the disease. Instead the men were told that they were being treated for "bad blood," which was a local 'catch all' term for a variety of maladies such as anemia or fatigue. The scientists did not treat the men for syphilis even after penicillin became available because they wanted to track the natural history of the disease. The study ran for over 40 shameful years.

Beginning in 1955, scientists at the Willowbrook State School on Staten Island (a New York mental institution housing severely mentally challenged individuals), conducted hepatitis studies that ran for almost 15 years. Hepatitis was a common health problem at Willowbrook with the risk of contracting the infection estimated at 30-50%. In one study, scientists gave a protective antibody to some individuals, but not others. In another study, they injected some newly admitted children with the protective antibody, while other newly admitted children were deliberately injected with the hepatitis virus. These children ultimately had to be segregated for the rest of their lives because the disease is contagious to others. Parents of the children gave consent for their children's participation in the experiments, but many argued that the true risks to their children weren't explained clearly and that there was inadequate disclosure of the specific details of the study.

There are numerous examples in history of such serious abuse including medical experiments on innocent victims by the Japanese military, to see how long it takes to freeze a man to death, or the German concentration camp experiments that had no medical value at all. These horrific experiments happened and apparently no one said, "Wait a minute. Is the pain and discomfort you are inflicting on these people worth the miniscule medical knowledge you will gain out of the experiment? Do the patients know what you will do to them and have they consented to participate in your experiment?" No, the scientists did not adequately inform the people that they would be subjects of experimentation, and they either never asked for their permission or garnered their participation through false pretenses. In all cases, the scientists felt that humanity absolutely needed the knowledge that would be gained from the experiment, and they felt that patients were not smart enough to understand the need for or nature of the experiment.

Along with these revelations about bioethics, we were also treated to lessons about genetics. Early in the 1990s, there was no Human Genome Project and genetic knowledge was very limited compared to today. Nevertheless, the President of the Cold Spring Harbor Laboratory was Nobel Laureate, James D. Watson, who with Francis Crick had co-discovered the double helix structure of DNA. Dr. Watson was Director of the laboratory for 35 years and the focus on genetic research was, and still is, firmly entrenched in the facility.

Over the years I was privileged to be invited back to Cold Spring Harbor's Banbury Center for other immersive learning experiences, including one week spent in a lab, actually isolating DNA and splicing a gene. But any time the lessons bordered on anything mathematical, I ceded control of the experiment to my classmates. However, the results of these mini-courses were very evident to me, particularly because so many science writers also attended the classes. I began to notice that the articles they wrote about genetics and scientific experiments on humans were more informative and knowledgeable.

Even today it is shameful how many newspaper and magazine writers are expected to write articles about scientific issues when they obviously do not understand science. Consequently, readers gain no useful knowledge from such articles or they believe the misinformation they read is actually fact. The knowledgeable science writers truly delve into the issues and can explain complicated scientific facts in understandable terms that non-scientists can understand. We definitely need more of them so that laymen do not misinterpret scientific information that they read about in the popular press. In fact, the public's misunderstanding of science is the leading reason that quacks and hustlers are able to fool the public into believing that they have the cure for whatever ails you, and you can have it... for a price.

Ultimately, I have served on many committees reviewing research programs and my focus has remained on the bioethical aspects of each experiment. Will patients be told what their possible benefits and risks will be? If they have a bad response to the experimental drug or device, who will pay for their medical care? If other patients were tested first, have doctors told the new patients what good and bad experiences happened to previous patients? Patients deserve to be told the truth so they will have realistic expectations. The days of eugenics are over. Everyone deserves honesty, compassion and the truth.

Most importantly, I have used the knowledge I gained at Cold Spring Harbor when we created NORD's medical research grant program. I felt it was our responsibility to assure that our grantees would follow ethical standards that their informed consent documents would be truthful and inclusive and there would be no conflicts-of-interest that might bias the outcome of the experiment. I could never look at a research proposal without reminding myself that my children had been research participants several times, and, if I thought that a doctor or hospital had not released the entire truth to me (including that some unknown side effects could possibly occur), I would not have allowed my children to participate in the experiment.

Being open, honest and fair are critically important to me. I expected (and felt the rare disease community deserved) the same treatment from the individuals and companies pursuing orphan drug development.

Chapter 9

A Constant Struggle

"I not only use all the brains that I have, but all that I can borrow."

Woodrow Wilson, 28th U.S. President

There are no easy answers. That is one of the things the Orphan Drug Act taught me. Ever since its passage, it has been a constant struggle to balance the needs of sick individuals and children against the ability of pharmaceutical companies to recoup their investment and be profitable. Sometimes that line is easy to draw and agreed upon by everyone; sometimes the line is drawn more like a line in the sand.

I heard that between the year 2000 and 2011, the anti-cholesterol drug Lipitor sold $121.4 billion in pills and the blood-thinning drug Plavix sold $74.6 billion. This illustrates the size of the potential markets for drugs that treat common health conditions along with their potential for profit. It will always be worthwhile to develop a drug for hypertension or arthritis that affect millions of people, even if you get just a small percentage of the market. On the other hand some orphan drug manufacturers expect their treatments to bring in huge sums of money even though they are sold only to small populations of people. This expectation is solely based on the price of the drug; if the price is high enough you can still obtain revenues of a billion dollars per year or more.

The United States is the only western industrialized country that does not control the price of drugs. This is why Canadians and Europeans spend so much less on pharmaceutical purchases. In the European Union, there are two steps to drug approval: First the European Medicines Agency (EMA) approves the drug so it can be sold in EU countries and then each country's national pricing authority decides whether they will pay for the drug, and at what price. If a drug is too expensive, a country can decide not to buy it and that's all there is to it. If a patient has a deadly disease with no other treatment options, the country can decide not to buy it until the patient is in the last stages of his or her disease. This has happened many times to people with some life threatening genetic diseases because the drug manufacturer refused to lower its price for expensive enzyme replacement therapies.

The first million-dollar treatment was approved in Europe for sale in 2013. It is a gene therapy treatment for a very rare disease, and the treatment is supposed to be a cure. Patients will need to get it only once in their lifetime, the company says, hence the enormous price. Would Jonas Salk say that about his polio vaccine? He didn't even bother to patent it because he wanted the whole world to benefit from his discovery. But hundreds of millions of humans needed the polio immunization treatments, whereas only a few dozen will need the million-dollar gene therapy infusion.

Something is wrong with this equation but I don't know how to put it into words. Time and again I go back in my mind to the Korean orphanage, thinking: "If we take all of your orphans (and give them good homes where they will be loved and will thrive), you will likely lose your business." Should I worry about the fate of that business? Or should I worry about saving those innocent babies whose lives will be ruined without stability, an education and a family who loves them? Is it morally acceptable for a company to price its treatment for a rare disease, higher than the price of treatment for a common disease, simply because the company wants to earn as much profit from the orphan drug as it would otherwise earn from a treatment for erectile dysfunction or arthritis?

So if a nation is faced with a high priced treatment that they cannot afford, should they throw caution to the wind and save that one child from certain death? Should they deny antibiotic treatments to hundreds or even thousands of children with ear infections in order to find enough money to treat one child with an expensive rare disease? Or should the drug company say, "OK, I'll give you the treatment at a lower cost because I know you can't afford it?" Where does human suffering end and compassion begin? To whom should we be asking these questions?

*

Rare disease drug prices are big news now and many orphan drug companies are feverishly analyzed and assessed by the financial press who measure success in terms of profits, not in terms of lives saved. But, the pharmaceutical industry's acceptance of the Orphan Drug Act and recognition that orphan drugs are worthy of adoption, took many years. I am reminded of the adage that, "You can lead a horse to water, but you can't make it drink." Instead the drug industry avoided orphan drugs for more than a decade after the law was enacted, until a few companies registered enormous profits on orphan drugs that attracted the attention of the rest of the industry. The first ten years after the Orphan Drug Act became law were slow in terms of drug companies recognizing the value of orphan drug designations. The big multinational pharmaceutical firms generally avoided treatments for limited numbers of patients, but young biotechnology companies saw the law as a major asset. Biotechnology enabled companies to develop important medical breakthroughs that could be grown in vats, in large commercial quantities. But patents for products that are made from biotechnology were sometimes not strong enough to prevent competition. Another manufacturer could make a similar product using a slightly different manufacturing process, and they could reach the market without violating the original manufacturer's patent. However, orphan drug exclusivity could prevent competition on "similar" drugs for seven certain years! Thus biotechnology companies were the first to recognize the importance of orphan drug exclusivity.

In the first decade of the Orphan Drug Act, biotechnology companies tended to utilize the law far more than the traditional pharmaceutical companies, except for one class of chemically based drugs. Traditional pharmaceutical companies often sought orphan drug designations for cancer therapies, and they still do. Every year cancer drugs have accounted for approximately 1/3 of all orphan drugs to reach the market.

At that time, people were surprised to learn that drugs for cancer would quality for a law designed to help rare diseases. They would ask me, "How can cancer fit the definition of an orphan disease?"
A cancer researcher once explained to me that there are over 200 different types of cancer, only five of them exceed the orphan disease population size of 200,000 Americans: breast cancer, prostate cancer, lung cancer, melanoma (a form of skin cancer) and a gastrointestinal (GI) cancer. These five cancers are so common they each affect millions of Americans, but all other types of cancer each effect fewer than 200,000 people in the United States.

For example, there is no single disease called "leukemia." Instead, the leukemias are a group of blood cancers, and the type of blood cell it affects, the symptoms it causes, and the treatments it will respond to characterizes each one. Each subtype of leukemia affects fewer than 200,000 people in the United States, but combined together all of the leukemias affect millions of people.

Oncologists very often treat cancer patients with drugs that FDA has approved for other types of cancer. If they have been treating a patient with a drug that initially works but then stops working on a person, they search around for any other cancer drugs that might work. Thus drug companies have long known that if they get a cancer drug on the market for one type of cancer, it will very likely be used on other types of cancer. Thus they sought, and received, orphan drug designations for many rare cancer drugs, which ultimately were prescribed for other cancer types. If drug companies would also conduct studies of their drug on other cancer types, they could then apply for additional orphan drug designations for every other rare type of cancer their drug was effective on. But many companies don't bother spending money on additional research because they know that oncologists will use the drug anyway for other types of cancer that are not listed on the drug's FDA approved label.

*

During the second decade of the Orphan Drug Act we began to notice that improved drugs were coming along for treatment of many diseases. If a new improved version of a drug gets on the market, the old original drug may not be needed as much. In a typical scenario a patient goes to their local pharmacy to refill a prescription and the pharmacist tells them she or he cannot get the drug because the company no longer manufactures it!

A good example of this would be animal derived insulin for diabetics. When biotechnology enabled companies to grow vats of insulin in factories, insulin manufacturers stopped taking insulin from cows and pigs. Eventually animal derived insulin became unavailable on the American market. However, the biotech insulin was safer but was much more expensive than the animal insulin. Many elderly diabetics were upset because they had been satisfactorily using the animal insulin for many years and could not afford the new biotech product.

In some cases neither the patient nor their doctor had any idea there was a new version of a drug on the market, and they were devastated when they could no longer purchase the original drug. In some cases, there was no competitive drug on the market; in these cases the manufacturer usually had a new management team making a business decision about low-revenue products. The corporate decision makers apparently did not understand some people's lives depended on the availability of the old drug (like Acthar Gel). But discontinuing the drug without giving any notice to patients and doctors gave them no time to search for alternative treatments (if there were any), and this was clearly inhumane!

So NORD supported a bill entitled "Notice of Discontinuance" which required orphan drug manufacturers to give at least one-year notice to the FDA that they intended to discontinue manufacture of an orphan drug. One year's notice would give FDA officials, members of the patient community and physicians ample time to find a new company who might adopt the drug, or find alternative treatments. For example, if another academic researcher was developing another drug for that disease, would the FDA allow patients access to that experimental drug? There were many possibilities if we only had ample time before the drug would disappear from pharmacies.

The big drug companies complained about the proposed "Notice of Discontinuance" because they saw it as a threat that might start with orphan drugs, but might ultimately affect their other products. They explained to me that they didn't want to make those types of corporate decisions public because they didn't want their competitors to know what they are doing or what they are planning on doing. But I explained that patients and doctors are not their competitors. They are human beings whose lives depend on their medicines, so the patients deserve to know when a company plans to stop making a drug. They were not manufacturing pantyhose, for heaven's sake! Thanks to NORD's Vice President of Public Policy in Washington D.C., Michael Langan, the "Notice of Discontinuance" for Orphan Drugs passed Congress and was signed into law. Then a few years later drug shortages began to occur for non-orphan drugs. In time, I noticed it overwhelmingly affected liquid drugs and in particular infused chemotherapy drugs for cancer patients and the FDA realized it could no longer keep quiet about the shortages. I worked with Michael, and tried to get a Notice of Discontinuance law enacted for all drugs, not just orphan drugs, but the industry put up a huge fight. In the end we agreed to a 6-month mandatory notice to the FDA, instead of one year. That compromise is still in force today.

Every week, the FDA now publishes on the Internet an electronic list of drugs that have been discontinued, are about to be discontinued, or are going to experience a shortage for many different reasons. The list gives doctors, pharmacists and patients advance notice of coming problems. When shortage problems are solved you can read about it on the same periodic email list so doctors and pharmacists can order the drug quickly from distributors or manufacturers.

The fact that so many of the drugs experiencing serious shortages have been cancer chemotherapy drugs that are administered intravenously, makes me wonder if the American public has been told the whole truth about the causes of these critical shortages.

The problems appear to be focused at factories that manufacture infused drugs that are liquids, and some of those factories appear to be unable to pass FDA inspections. But no one has been able to pin down a standard reason for all of these shortages, and our concern is not the mystery. Our concern is the patients and the Notice of Discontinuance continues to give them a fair shot at locating therapeutic options before they have no options.

*

Because so many orphan drugs are for rare types of cancer, it makes sense that the first major American revolt against cancer drug pricing came from oncologists. Usually, academic medical professionals work closely with the pharmaceutical industry because they need industry support for conducting clinical trials. So when oncologists spoke out against the cost of new cancer drugs, they knew they were risking future financial support from the industry.

The revolt was started by a newspaper op-ed column written by oncologists from one of New York's leading cancer hospitals, and it morphed into an effort by hundreds of cancer specialists from more than 15 countries on 5 continents. They were mostly leukemia specialists upset at pharmaceutical prices they believed to be "astronomical, unsustainable and perhaps even immoral." ("Doctors Denounce Cancer Drug Prices of $100,000 a year", by Andrew Pollack, NY Times, April 25, 2013).

A breakthrough cancer drug from the Swiss pharmaceutical company Novartis, with the brand name Gleevec, got on the American market in 2001 for chronic myeloid leukemia. It was an orphan drug priced at $30,000 per year. By 2013 the price had tripled, even though Gleevec had competition from five newer drugs, but they were even more expensive.

When the cancer specialists published their op-ed in the *NY Times* they were complaining about a newly approved drug called Zaltrap, manufactured by a French company, Sanofi. The doctors' article resulted in Sanofi cutting the price of Zaltrap in half, thus their effort was successful.

The news article signed by 120 doctors, and published in a medical journal, asked how much is enough; if Novartis sales of Gleevec are $3 billion a year, could the company get by with sales of $2 billion? "When do you cross the line from essential profits to profiteering?" asked one researcher. Sales of Gleevec in 2012 were $4.7 billion, even though its orphan drug exclusivity had expired.

The company says it gives the drug for free to 5,000 uninsured or underinsured Americans each year, and provides it for free to 50,000 people in low-income (third world) countries. Novartis has also underwritten research to get Gleevec approved for other types of cancer such as myelodysplastic syndromes/myeloproliferative diseases, adult lymphocytic leukemia, aggressive systemic mastocytosis, hypereosinophilic syndromes, and dermatofibrosarcoma. However, the journal article written by cancer doctors, points out that prices for drugs in the United States are twice as high as most other industrialized countries, because the United States does not use government price controls.

One doctor who was an author of the article feels his research career will likely be hurt because of the article complaining about cancer drug prices. He opined, "Pharmaceutical companies have lost their moral sense… (it is) getting to the point where it (drug pricing) is becoming unsustainable."

But I think back to the time when I begged some drug companies, such as Amgen, not to price their drugs outrageously, because they would ultimately put the whole orphan drug program in jeopardy.

"Just be reasonable," I asked them, so politicians would not make a target out of orphan drugs when they complain about the rising costs of health care. But now rare cancer drugs are in the crosshairs. The companies continue to tell Wall Street that they expect to earn billions of dollars from sales of orphan drugs to small populations of cancer patients, and they continue to tell politicians that their profits are reasonable. Thus they brag about big profits to Wall Street, and deny big profits to politicians.

I can only wonder when the drug industry will realize that when they brag about profits to Wall Street that patients, doctors and politicians also read those predictions. No one likes being made into a fool, particularly when the profits of those companies are coming primarily from American consumers. We Americans are subsidizing the success and growth of the worldwide pharmaceutical industry because the rest of the world refuses to pay the asking prices for their medicines. Maybe, like the owner of the Korean orphanage, some of these companies see patients as commodities and have forgotten that they are sick people, trying to outlive a death sentence. They only want to feel better, enjoy one more birthday, or live to see the birth of a healthy grandchild.

Thus, the main ingredient of the Orphan Drug Act that has made it so successful is the ability of a company to earn huge profits from their orphan drug. The main ingredient that threatens the Orphan Drug Act is the possibility that orphan drugs will earn larger and larger slices of the healthcare financial pie. It is a conundrum!

*

The pharmaceutical industry may show no restraint as they continue to push the price of drugs higher and higher, but other people are noticing and they have started to make noise.

By the summer of 2014, two important events catapulted orphan drugs again into the headlines, casting uncertainties about the future of orphan drug policies in the United States. The first was an article in the *New York Times* ("A Dearth in Innovation for Key Drugs", NYT-July 22, 2014; Eduardo Porter), and the second was news about a miraculous new cure for hepatitis C (Washington Post, July 24, 2014; "The Drug That's Forcing America's Most Important- and Uncomfortable- Health Care Debate", by Jason Millman). The cost of that drug threatened to bankrupt state Medicaid programs because the price of the medicine was too high, and too many hepatitis C patients were poor Medicaid recipients.

The first article generally decried the success of the Orphan Drug Act in attracting pharmaceutical companies into developing drugs for rare diseases at the expense of luring the drug industry away from researching new treatments for common health conditions. In particular, the author resented the absence of incentives that would lure drug companies into developing new antibiotics.

Quoting Professor Michael S. Kinch from the Yale Center for Molecular Discovery, who tracked the evolution of pharmaceutical development over the past two centuries, the article noted that pharmaceutical firms are generally developing new treatments for health conditions that affect small numbers of people. "More people are studying orphan diseases than have orphan diseases," said the professor "jokingly", according to the article. I didn't think his statement was funny. Those stinging words felt like listening to people complain that too many minority students were being admitted to colleges, and because of affirmative action there isn't enough room left for white middle class students. Why is the majority so invested in keeping minorities powerless?

Some of the major factors that lure the interest of drug companies to orphan drugs, according to the *New York Times* article, is willingness of health insurance companies to pay very high prices for a drug that is used to treat a small population of patients; the cost of research and development is cheaper because clinical trials are smaller; and since so many orphan drugs are biologics, not chemical medicines, FDA's slow approval of generic biologics keeps a monopoly functioning longer for the inventing company.

Patricia Danzon of the Wharton School of the University of Pennsylvania was quoted as saying, "The decks have been stacked in favor of orphan drugs." According to Professor Danzon, "There's a myth in the United States that market forces are working to control prices. It's clear that they aren't."

The *New York Times* article was the first time I heard or read about resentment against the development of treatments for rare diseases. There was no mention of the fact that for the first ten years, only a handful of companies were willing to consider orphan drugs in their research pipeline; for the second decade biotechnology companies became interested in orphan drugs; and in the third decade of the Orphan Drug Act the pharmaceutical and biologics industries finally recognized that the law made the development of treatments for rare diseases worth their while. After 32 years, in 2014, the envy and resentment finally reared its ugly head showing that some people still believe that health resources should be reserved for the benefit of the masses, at the expense of minorities.

The second article that struck me was printed in the *Washington Post*, and it was NOT about a rare disease or an orphan drug. A small drug company called Gilead Sciences, Inc. developed a CURE for hepatitis C, which would compete with Olysio®, a drug the FDA had approved to treat hepatitis C in November of 2013. The second drug, named Sovaldi®, was approved by the FDA in December 2013 and the price was higher than the first drug. The cost of Sovaldi was pegged at $84,000 for a 12-week course of treatment.

According to the Centers for Disease Control (CDC), about 3.2 million Americans have hepatitis C. A large number of that population are low-income individuals and therefore qualify for Medicaid, the government health program for poor people. Many people contract hepatitis C from intravenous drug abuse (specifically sharing needles) and many contracted the disease in jail. Before Sovaldi became available the disease was treated with weekly injections of interferon for 48 weeks, but the cure rate was only 50%.

When Congress passed ObamaCare, a primary target was to provide insurance coverage for millions of poor people who did not previously qualify for Medicaid or Medicare. So they broadened the rules to extend Medicaid to millions more needy people who had income just above the poverty line. But Medicaid is a unique program that is funded by both state and federal funds. So when Sovaldi was approved states realized that they could not afford to pay $84,000 for each hepatitis C patient in their state who was now covered by Medicaid.

Tom Burns, an Oregon Medicaid official told the *Washington Post* that it would cost $360 million a year to provide Sovaldi to Medicaid patients with hepatitis C in Oregon! But in 2013 Oregon paid only $377 million for their entire Medicaid prescription drug bill to treat 600,000 Medicaid beneficiaries with all diagnoses in that state. Meanwhile Gilead reported to Wall St. that in the first 3 months on the American market Sovaldi sold $2.3 billion, and in the second quarter the drug's sales were $3.5 billion.

How much is enough?

Medicaid officials and health insurers across the nation are alarmed at the price of Sovaldi, but the company says it's a cure, not a treatment, so the cost is worth it. One Medicaid official said they are used to high prices for orphan drugs that treat 500 patients in a state, not hundreds of thousands, or millions of people. He called the price of Sovaldi "a game changer." Oregon has added a few hundred thousand people to its Medicaid roll since ObamaCare took effect, and the program now covers almost 1 million people. No one knows exactly how many of those people have hepatitis C.

Evidently, no one explained to pharmaceutical companies that **they cannot use orphan drug pricing for drugs that are aimed at large populations of people**. I worry that people will simply assume that Sovaldi is an orphan drug because of its pricing, and the Orphan Drug Act will have to be defended again and again. On the other hand Sovaldi may serve as a wake-up call for the American Congress who, until now, has refused to allow the government to negotiate prices for Medicare drugs. Eventually, we will have to give the American government power to regulate drug prices because the industry is unable to police itself. Sovaldi is **NOT** an orphan drug!

Chapter 10

International Impact

"Saints are sinners who kept on going."

Robert Louis Stevenson

I often became so focused on an issue that I was like a horse running a race with blinders on----not looking left or right, but totally focused on the next disease, the next treatment, and the next obstacles I would have to defeat before those patients could be helped. Too often I failed to recognize that other people were running that race too. People who could help even if their positions or jobs might initially seem counter to my efforts and the mission of NORD.

One such person was Larry Weaver, Ph.D., who was a pharmacist by training. He became the Dean of the School of Pharmacy at the University of Minnesota. After he retired he decided to take a job at the Pharmaceutical Manufacturers Association (PMA----now known as PhRMA) in Washington, D.C. He stayed in this temporary job for approximately 10 years.

After the PMA dropped its opposition to the Orphan Drug Act, and after the legislation became law, PMA wanted to appear as if it was cooperating on the orphan drug issue. It created an internal orphan drug committee composed of member company representatives, and invited myself and Marlene Haffner of the FDA to attend the meetings, even though we were not voting members of the group. We could provide information to the companies about drugs that were looking for commercial sponsors. Larry Weaver was assigned as the PMA staff person responsible for the meetings, and George Goldstein, M.D., of Sterling Drug, was a committee member. It was Goldstein who I had called when problems arose with the Israeli drug for multiple sclerosis, which eventually became Copaxone.

At the PMA meetings we talked about a wide variety of drugs, including biologics. The medicines would not help patients if they could not get on the market, and companies were needed to make them commercially available. Larry Weaver always made it a point to say hello to me and ask if I had heard of any more drugs looking for sponsors. He was eager to help in any way possible.

I had no idea that Larry had become infected with a passion for orphan drugs that would last the rest of his life. With my "blinders" on I simply didn't recognize Larry's passion for our cause. All I remember from that time was a nice grandfatherly man and my own single-mindedness. Although I may have initially missed Larry's devotion to the orphan drug movement, he became a valuable ally and a trusted friend. He also became one of the driving forces to make orphan drugs an international cause, spreading them throughout the world.

After working a decade in Washington, Larry and his wife Dee decided to travel. Dee wanted Larry to retire when he left the University of Minnesota's pharmacy school, but instead he joined the PMA and worked for another decade, so he owed her a real retirement with lots of travel. I could always count on getting a Christmas letter from Dee when they were truly retired, explaining what they had been up to and where they had traveled. It seemed wherever they went on their foreign trips Larry tried to see government health officials so he could talk to them about orphan drugs.

The first country that Larry convinced to do something about orphan drugs was Singapore. A hospital pharmacist complained to Larry that when they needed an orphan drug from America, it would get tied up in Singapore's Customs office for several weeks. Often the patient would greatly deteriorate or die before the drug could reach the hospital. Larry convinced the government of Singapore to enact a law that exempted imported orphan drugs from the U.S. being delayed by red tape in their Customs bureau. If a doctor in Singapore needed a drug that was an officially designated orphan drug in the United States, he or she could order it and it would be shipped directly to the doctor at the hospital. Because of Larry Weaver's efforts the drug would no longer get caught in the endless delays of Singapore's Customs bureau, and patients could be treated immediately.

After Singapore, Japan enacted its own Orphan Drug law in 1993, which subsidized the cost of the drugs' development in Japan, but it did not include other financial incentives. The Japanese apparently did not recognize that the main reason for the success of the American legislation has always been its financial incentives, most especially the seven years of exclusivity during which no other drug company can compete with the same orphan drug for the same rare disease. Without financial incentives companies would not generally care about getting a rare disease treatment on the market in other countries, and big companies like Pfizer or Merck did not need a subsidy to pay for their research on an orphan drug.

Several other Asian countries followed Japan's and Singapore's examples, and then in 2000 the European Union (EU) passed its "Orphan Drug Regulation" which largely followed the financial incentives of the American law. Marlene Haffner and I advised the European Union on the development of their law explaining what should be included or omitted in their orphan drug regulation because we knew what worked and what didn't work in the American law.

When I began fighting for the passage of the Orphan Drug Act, I never expected that my efforts would eventually take me around the globe. There were several trips to Europe, and particularly Paris, leading up to passage of the EU "Orphan Drug Regulation." On many of those trips to Europe I had the privilege to observe Dr. Haffner in her secret life as champion shopper and tourist. On one trip to Brussels she convinced me to take a quick train ride with her to the small town of Bruges in Belgium, where the scenery was extraordinary and a hospital from the Middle Ages was still standing. Wherever Marlene was in Belgium she looked for lace and she came home with ample supplies of lace for her friends and relatives.

In every country Marlene knew what to shop for. She loved Belgian lace but I was only interested in Belgian chocolate, an affordable indulgence that my family greatly appreciated.

*

The effort to pass orphan drug legislation in Europe started during the 1990s. It started with the recognition that an organized effort was needed to unite the political influence of many rare disease charities in all European countries. Eventually, a new organization modeled on the coalition that NORD represented in the United States was created. The organization, known as EURORDIS (European Organization for Rare Diseases), was based in Paris in offices donated by the French Muscular Dystrophy Society.

EURORDIS is like a community organizer on a grand scale. After 2000, when the European Union's Orphan Drug Regulation became law, EURORDIS continued to unite European rare disease support groups in each EU country to ensure that they remained a political power monitoring health policy in each country. As the iron curtain across Europe fell, more countries were added to the European Union, and rare disease support groups in each country needed to be organized to ensure that emerging health policies would not omit the priorities of rare disease patients and families.

EURORDIS has done a spectacular job across a continent that speaks many different languages in twenty-eight member states, because it understands that cultural issues that divide us are counterbalanced by the issues that unite people with rare diseases around the world.

*

Invariably, there were differences between the U.S. and EU rare disease laws. One major difference is that the European regulation awards 10 years of exclusive marketing rights for an orphan drug, whereas the American law provides seven years of exclusivity. But the main difference between the American and European health care system has always been the financial reimbursement structure. In America, private health insurance companies usually pay for prescription drugs for workers who have employer sponsored insurance policies, the elderly (age 65 and older) and people who become disabled in their adult life have Medicare, while Medicaid pays for people living in poverty. Uninsured Americans have no choice but to pay cash. At the time, however, Medicare did not have a prescription drug benefit. Instead most retirees and disabled people had to pay cash for their prescription drugs.

In Europe, however, national health insurance was mandated in every EU nation, so in most cases national governments were the payers for all pharmaceuticals. Those governments jealously guarded their healthcare expenses, and they certainly wanted to guard against the very high prices that some drug companies were charging for their orphan drugs in the U.S.

Thus a provision was placed in the European law, similar to the Metzenbaum orphan drug amendment that was passed by the U.S. Congress and then vetoed by the first President Bush, allowing the EU government to withdraw an orphan drug designation under certain circumstances. In particular, one member nation of the European Union would have to trigger a review of the drug's orphan status after its 6th year on the market, and explain why the drug should lose the remainder of its 10 years of exclusivity. Such judgments would be based on profitability of the drug; if it was no longer a drug of limited commercial value then it would no longer deserve protection from competition. If the drug's EU sales record showed it was a drug of substantial commercial value, it could lose the last 3 or 4 years of its exclusivity.

As far as I know, up to 2013 no European country had triggered the review for any orphan drug in the EU. Instead, if they did not like the price of an orphan drug, the national health reimbursement authorities simply decided not to pay for it. Thus a two-step system for orphan drugs evolved in Europe: first, the drug must be approved for sale by the EMA (the European government's equivalent of the American FDA) based on proof of safety and effectiveness, and second, each individual country's health authority decides whether or not to pay for the drug. It is not unusual for an orphan drug to be approved for sale in Europe, but not be available to patients in certain countries because their reimbursement authority decided not to pay for it.

Member nations of the European Union use various methods to keep drug prices under control. Unlike the "free market" American system which requires buyers to pay any price the manufacturer asks for the drug, most European countries have a mathematical formula that requires the price of a drug to be calculated on the average price the company sells its drug in other industrialized countries. Even though the drug gets approved for sale by a centralized European bureau (the EMA), each country's reimbursement authority can independently decide whether or not they will pay for the drug, and the amount it is willing to pay. So it is possible that only some or none of the European countries will agree to pay for a specific orphan drug, even though the drug is technically "approved" for sales throughout Europe. And the drug will be approved for sale in some European countries when the manufacturer agrees to compromise on a lower price that is more affordable than the original asking price.

*

When I began the push for the Orphan Drug Act, the issue was a personal one; one that I understood specifically in relation to the United States. I never imagined, nor desired, to become involved in the orphan drug struggle in other countries. The laws were different. The companies were different. The politics were different. But the families and the children, and their stories were the same. When people called me needing help, people whose struggles I understood intimately, how could I say no?

Shortly after the EU's law went into effect I received a phone call from the French Muscular Dystrophy Association asking me to come to Paris and appear on their telethon. The American Muscular Dystrophy Association held annual telethons around Labor Day ever since I was a child, and they always raised millions of dollars. Thus, similar European charities representing muscular dystrophy also held annual telethons that raised a lot of money, but the French group was particularly successful and was able to sponsor research on many genetic diseases. When its area of concern broadened to include many other hereditary diseases, the public could more easily identify with the charity even if they knew nobody with muscular dystrophy.

In response to their invitation I asked when the telethon was scheduled. When they told me the date, I told them I could not be there because I was scheduled to testify before Congress at that time. When I hung up the phone I thought that would be the end of it, but I received several more phone calls that day from Paris begging me to change my plans and come to Paris. But Congressional testimony is nothing to sneeze at, and since at that time we had no staff in Washington who could substitute for me, I could not cancel the testimony.

Finally a person from the French Muscular Dystrophy organization called again and asked me if I would be willing to fly to Paris in the supersonic transport, the Concorde! Only British Air and Air France flew the Concorde, primarily because it was so expensive to fly that the price of Concorde tickets were unaffordable for most travelers. Nevertheless, passengers on the Concorde arrived in Paris three hours after taking off from New York. There was not even enough time to get jet lag on the Concorde.

"What time is scheduled for your testimony on that date?" asked the caller from Paris. I told her the time and she proceeded to calculate that if she booked me on a returning Concorde flight to Dulles National Airport, near Washington DC, I could make it to Capitol Hill in ample time to testify. I had heard that a ticket on the Concorde could cost as much as $8,000, so I asked if it was that important for a charity to spend all of that money. "Yes," she answered, "Besides we have connections to people at the airline so we won't be spending a lot of money."

My excuses were gone, and there was nothing more to say except, "OK." On the prescribed date I went to JFK Airport in New York and got on the Concorde. I was surprised to see that the interior was like a long narrow tube with only two seats on each side of the plane. A tall man would not be able to stand erect in the tube because the ceiling was too low.

There were only two compartments inside the plane: half of the vehicle was the front compartment which had very few passengers (about five or six). The second compartment was the back of the vehicle where I was to sit. There was no other passenger in my section of the plane until a few minutes before they closed the doors. A frazzled man, who looked like he ran through the airport at top speed just to arrive before the doors were closed, stomped into the rear compartment of the plane wearing a beret and carrying a dog. He seemed very upset and spoke English with a thick accent. "I will never come to America again!" he announced passionately, "They will not allow my dog in the restaurants. What kind of country is this?"

The flight attendant agreed with him, fully understanding why he was riled up, and spoke softly in French to the unkempt man. Then she brought him wine, and more wine, and a meal that didn't resemble ordinary airline food, and food for the man's dog, and more wine. He and the dog fell asleep for the rest of the trip.

When I arrived in Paris three hours later a driver was waiting for me and took me to the studio where the telethon was to be broadcast. It was very close to the Eiffel Tower. I spent time in make-up and then when I was waiting back stage a woman came over to me with a piece of paper. "Here is your speech," she said. I looked at the paper and it was written in French. I told her, "I cannot read French. I don't speak French, so I cannot read this." She said, "Oh. Well we can write it phonetically." "No thank you," I said. "I have to speak English." "You cannot," said the woman. "Only French is allowed to be broadcast on French television," she said definitively.

I was grateful for that piece of information, because I finally understood why I could not find any English speaking TV channels in my hotel room whenever I spent a few days in Paris. It took several more years before French TV, at least in hotels, carried BBC news and sometimes CNN. But the telethon crew appeared so amazed when I said "No" to them that I wondered whether I was triggering an international incident. "Perhaps other Europeans learn French when they go to school," I said, "but in America the continents primarily speak Spanish. I learned a little Spanish in school, but not French. And if I speak it phonetically I will sound like an idiot, and your audience won't understand a thing I say."

In the end they decided that I could speak in English and they would substantially reduce the power on my microphone so I could not be heard while a translator would speak over me in French. Then suddenly someone explained to me in English that for the entire day people with rare diseases were walking through Paris and each parade would merge into one giant group at the Eiffel Tower. The doors of the studio would open and the marchers would walk into the theater carrying signs revealing which disease they represented. It was quite extraordinary. It felt like they were trying to capture the mood of the second Quincy episode when they filmed the mock march on Washington in Pasadena. Even though I did not speak French I could translate the disease names on the signs the parents carried: Marfan syndrome, epidermolysis bullosa, hemophilia, etc. I was stunned, and quite grateful that I did not have to deliver a speech that no one would understand.

A few hours later I landed in Washington very tired but without jet lag, just in time to deliver my congressional presentation.

*

Meanwhile, Larry Weaver and his wife Dee continued to hopscotch across the world. When they traveled to Sweden they visited an entrepreneur named Lars-Uno Larsson. Lars caught the contagious orphan drug bug from Larry, and in 1998 he opened a new company called Swedish Orphan International AB. His concept was to open country- specific orphan drug companies throughout the world, and pretty soon Orphan Europe, Orphan Japan, Orphan Australia, Orphan USA and several others were launched.

In time there were disagreements between Swedish Orphan and some of its member companies, and some of the companies became independent from the Swedish parent company (e.g., Orphan Europe, Orphan USA, etc.). Even though they changed their corporate names in several countries, they have all maintained their singular devotion to rare disease treatments.

Larry Weaver agreed to serve on Swedish Orphan's Board of Directors, and it wasn't long before he and his friend Bert Spilker, Ph.D., started Orphan Medical, Inc. in his home state of Minnesota. Bert had worked for large American multinational pharmaceutical firms, such as Burroughs Wellcome, before joining Orphan Medical. It was because of Larry and Bert that some of the most important lingering orphan drugs were finally adopted. Orphan Medical was eventually sold and became Jazz Pharmaceuticals, but still specializes in orphan drugs.

Sadly, in the first decade of 2000 we learned that Larry was suffering from Alzheimer's disease. Dee still traveled with him for a while, and people could not help but notice how Larry was aging. When he died, I believe Larry was in his late 80s or early 90s, and he had accomplished more in his lifetime than other people could ever imagine. A building at the University of Minnesota's School of Pharmacy is named after him, and I hope the students who attend that school will understand how important Larry Weaver was to the international orphan drug movement.

*

The Orphan Drug Act would also impact our neighbors to the north. I cannot talk about the law's impact in Canada without talking about Eric Gervais. Among the unbelievable characters I've met in my life, Eric is a singular phenomenon. A tall, good looking French Canadian with a charming accent, I first met Eric in New York City at a meeting he requested, with hope that I could help him. He worked for a Canadian generic drug manufacturer, Duchesnay, near Montreal. But the topic of our meeting had nothing to do with generic drugs.

Eric's company was manufacturing an old drug to treat severe morning sickness in pregnant women. Pregnant women are not rare and having had three children, I knew that morning sickness was very common. However, the drug that Eric wanted to get FDA approval for was Bendectin, which had been voluntarily taken off the American market in 1983.

Bendectin was first introduced on the American market in 1956. It was estimated that at least 33 million pregnant women had taken Bendectin for morning sickness before women began to submit law suits against the drug's manufacturer, Merrell Dow, claiming that the drug caused birth defects in their children. The drug was simply a mixture of an over-the-counter antihistamine and a vitamin, so Merrell Dow fought each law suit vigorously – and the company won every case. The cost of defending itself against each lawsuit led them to decide to stop manufacturing the drug because it cost them too much to defend themselves. Bendectin was voluntarily taken off the American market in 1983, even though there was no evidence that it caused birth defects.

Although the drug was not available in the U.S., Duchesnay had been manufacturing and selling the drug in Canada for several years without any problems. But the U.S. is a litigious country and because no company had put the drug back on the U.S. market, there was no FDA approved treatment for morning sickness on the American market. Eric wanted to get the drug on the U.S. market for the most severe form of morning sickness, known as hyperemesis gravidarum. Eric had asked the FDA's Office for Orphan Product Development for an orphan drug designation, but it was refused. I asked Dr. Marlene Haffner why, she told me she had talked to her husband about the drug because he was an obstetrician and gynecologist. He felt if the drug ever got back on the American market, all obstetricians would likely prescribe it because there has been no other adequate morning sickness treatment available for doctors to treat women who suffer incredibly and sometimes have to be hospitalized because of constant vomiting.

Around that time my administrative assistant, Audrey Ashley, told me her daughter was pregnant and was suffering incredibly from morning sickness. A few weeks later, her daughter had to be hospitalized because of dehydration. Then under the pressure from her insurance carrier, the hospital released her and said she could be treated at home. That meant a nurse had to come to her house and set up an intravenous line and then show Audrey, her mother, how to operate the system so that she could give her daughter the infused medicine. The grandmother, with no medical training, was expected to treat her pregnant daughter, all in the name of economy.

But if the insurer really wanted to save money, it should have been lobbying to bring Bendectin back instead of treating severe morning sickness with expensive intravenous therapy. Sometimes economy wastes more than it saves.

Thus, Eric launched the effort to get his morning sickness drug back on the U.S. market. He needed American clinical trials proving it was a safe and effective drug, which took millions of dollars and years of work. But Eric would call us from time to time, and since he was interested in our orphan drug work, he decided to come to NORD's meetings and participate in discussions with companies that were developing orphan drugs. Mostly, he listened to what other manufacturers said and what they were doing in preparation for launch of their orphan drugs. He asked questions to learn how they could find patients for clinical trials and how they could identify leading researchers to do research on the target disease. He did all this even though he was not developing any orphan drugs.

Looking back I asked him, "Eric, how come you are so interested in our corporate meetings even though you don't have an orphan drug?" He could not verbalize why he came except that he felt accepted by the other companies. Big pharmaceutical companies wouldn't talk to him when he went to their meetings but small companies were predominant at our meetings and they welcomed him. At our meetings, he monitored the progress of other manufacturers. They asked him questions about the Canadian market, about which they knew little. The Canadian market was considered to be so small it was hardly worth thinking about for multi-national drug companies. Since Canada had no orphan drug law, there were no incentives to entice drug companies into the Canadian market.

Apparently, however, one day Eric had a vision of creating a Canadian orphan drug company that would adopt American and European orphan drugs and get them approved for sale in Canada.

He called me up and asked, "What do you think?" "I think it's a fantastic idea, Eric. I'll help you," I said. Eric created Medunik Canada, and licensed orphan drugs from European and American companies. Most of them are now in clinical trials for approval by Health Canada. Many of them can be prescribed even before they are approved for marketing because Canada has a Special Access Program (SAP), allowing orphan drugs to be prescribed to named patients with serious and life threatening diseases when there are no alternative treatments available. Finally, someone is taking care of Canada, one of the last hold-outs in the industrialized world that has never enacted orphan drug legislation.

Dr. Marlene Haffner had tried mightily over the years to get Health Canada to see the light, but she was never able to move the government bureaucracy. I don't think they will remain immovable for long thanks to Eric Gervais. His drug for morning sickness, which his company named Diclegis for the U.S. market, was finally approved by the FDA in April 2013, after Eric worked for 18 years to get it approved for sale in the United States. It is not an orphan drug technically, but it has fueled orphan drug availability in Canada for people with rare diseases simply because it was the impetus for forming Medunik. And in 2013, Health Canada finally announced that it will issue orphan drug regulations to ease availability of orphan drugs in Canada, even if there will still be no incentives to entice companies into the Canadian market.

Chapter 11

Entrepreneurs

"If I have seen further than others, it is by standing upon the shoulders of giants."

Sir Isaac Newton, British scientist

One great thing about entrepreneurs is that they are often ahead of the curve. The established (and inflexible) pharmaceutical giants may have fought against the passage of the ODA and then ignored its application, but many entrepreneurs recognized the law's promise. Instinctively they knew if they used the law correctly they could very possibly hit a home run.

One day, a New Jersey man named Sol Barer came to visit. When we started talking I knew immediately that I liked this man. He was open and honest. I felt that it was against his nature to lie about something or embellish facts with half-truths. Sol announced that he recently started a new company in New Jersey called Celgene, and was conducting clinical trials on thalidomide, of all things!

As I've discussed previously, thalidomide was originally developed in Europe as a tranquilizer and treatment for morning sickness in pregnant women, but instead resulted in horrible birth defects when taken during pregnancy. The drug was never approved in the U.S. and after the connection to birth defects was recognized thalidomide was banned worldwide in the 1960s.

In my travels I learned a lot about thalidomide because it was known to have some important medical uses for a variety of diagnoses, but no one would manufacture it because it was virtually uninsurable! The European manufacturer had paid out millions of dollars in settlements to the people who were so grievously harmed by thalidomide. No insurance company would have a thing to do with that drug. Nevertheless, any harm done by thalidomide was primarily in the developing fetuses of pregnant women. In adults, thalidomide can cause some serious side effects such as peripheral neuropathy, but such side effects are common for many potent drugs. If thalidomide could be beneficial in treating serious diseases, did that merit bringing the drug back? For some doctors, the answer was yes. The disorder that brought thalidomide back was serious and had a reputation as infamous as thalidomide itself.

An American doctor told me that a hospital in Israel was treating people with thalidomide who had advanced leprosy. Apparently, in 1964 (a few years after thalidomide was banned worldwide), an Israeli physician named Jacob Sheskin had, through serendipity, discovered a beneficial use for the drug for people with leprosy. Due to terrible pain from the destruction of their nerves, they were unable to sleep. Dr. Sheskin found out that his hospital had some leftover thalidomide in storage and because it was a tranquilizer (and because he realized there were no pregnant women in his leprosy patients) he used the drug to calm his patients and reduce their pain.

The doctor found that his patients not only slept soundly because the pain went away, but three days later a serious skin complication known as erythema nodosum completely cleared up! Discussing this progress with his colleagues, they reasoned that the drug did not allow nerves to grow, explaining why so many babies were born without arms and legs when their mothers ingested thalidomide during early pregnancy. They also knew that many cancerous tumors thrived on blood circulating from blood vessels. They suggested if blood could be stopped from circulating in tumors it might cause tumors to shrink or even disappear. When they published their findings in medical journals, the news flew around the world quickly and other geographic areas where leprosy occurs tried to get thalidomide or make it themselves. The theories about cancer and tumor growth would have to wait.

One of these areas was Brazil, doctors there found thalidomide to be indispensable for leprosy patients. They could not buy the drug from a pharmaceutical company (because no drug company would manufacture it) so they manufactured the drug themselves. Unfortunately, they sent many of the patients back into the bush with thalidomide pills, and when their spouse saw how relaxed and pain free they were, they decided to share the medicine. Soon there were thalidomide babies being born in Brazil and other third world countries. So the absolute need of restricting distribution of the drug became paramount again, decades after the initial thalidomide babies were born in Europe.

There are a small number of leprosy patients in the United States mostly around the Gulf Coast and a Public Health Hospital in Louisiana knew the importance of thalidomide for these patients. They made the drug by hand because there was no way to buy it. On a trip to France and Belgium in

1990, I mentioned this to a pharmaceutical executive and he immediately reacted: "Shh!" he cautioned. "Don't mention that drug in Europe unless you want to start riots in the street!"

Now Sol Barer was walking into my office and announcing that he was developing thalidomide not only for leprosy, but for a malignant blood disease, multiple myeloma. He was also studying the drug for treatment of a group of life threatening blood diseases known as myelodysplastic syndromes.

Sol was eager to speak about his research and his vision for the future of his company. I told him about a few other diseases that might be helped by thalidomide, but I had a question: "Sol," I asked, "Do you have insurance? Have you found an insurer willing to cover a company that makes thalidomide?"

Sol thought a moment and responded, "Well, no company will insure us now, but if someone sues us now what will they get? Three desks and a copy machine? That's what they'll get, because we have nothing. But I do have a letter from an insurance company promising that they will insure us when we get the drug on the market."

The answer that Sol gave me that day is the very essence of the entrepreneur. He did get thalidomide (Thalomid) on the market, he did put strict warnings on the drug to prevent pregnant women from using it, he did get insurance for the company, and then he developed off-shoots of thalidomide, such as Revlimid, for other rare forms of cancer. Today Celgene is one of the most successful mid-size biotechnology companies that took a very risky chance and hit a home run.

*

Another entrepreneur who took a chance was Abe Abuchowski, a professor from a New Jersey university who was convinced he could coat a molecule with polyethylene glycol (PEG) and make the medicine last a very long time. This was more than a biotechnology drug, but a potential new drug delivery system and, much like orphan drugs, the pharmaceutical industry initially wanted no part of it. Since the pharmaceutical industry couldn't be enticed to invest in PEG, Abe started his own company in 1982 and called it Enzon.

To prove his theory Abe chose one of the rarest diseases known to medicine: severe combined immune deficiency (SCID), caused by a shortage of an enzyme called adenosine deaminase (ADA). There are many types of SCID, but SCID-ADA amounts to only 15% of all SCID cases (less than 100 cases in the United States). One of the reasons that SCID-ADA is so rare is that children born with this genetic defect usually die in infancy because they cannot fight off common infections. SCID-ADA is also known as "the Bubble Boy disease" because a movie had been made in the 1960s or 70s about a boy with SCID-ADA who was raised in a sterile plastic bubble in order to prevent infections from killing him.

Abe coated the ADA enzyme, obtained from cows, with polyethylene glycol and gave it to about 10 children with SCID-ADA. The children developed immunity to common infections. When they got a cold it did not turn into pneumonia, and some even recovered from chicken pox, which ordinarily killed children with this genetic defect. The PEG coating slowed the clearance of the bovine ADA and reduced the immune system's response against it. This allowed the medication to achieve its full effects by maintaining high levels of ADA. PEG-ADA was expensive so we ran a MAP program for the drug to ensure that patients would continue to get it even if they had no health insurance.

Despite the success and potential of PEGylation for the ADA enzyme, the pharmaceutical industry still wasn't interested. They considered the success of Enzon's drug an anomaly. To get more funds for investment Enzon went on the stock market, probably too soon.

On a Phil Donahue Show in the early 1990's (L to R) actor Dick Van Dyke, Abbey Meyers and Phil Donahue. Mr. Van Dyke had lost a grandchild to Reye's syndrome and he wanted to warn parents that children can get Reye's Syndrome from ingesting aspirin when they get sick. Ultimately the FDA finally required a warning printed on aspirin labels about the link between aspirin and Reye's Syndrome.

The second drug that PEGylation was tried on was L-asparaginase, which was manufactured by Merck and was used to treat some rare childhood leukemias. L-asparaginase starves and destroys leukemic cancer cells (anti-leukemic effect) by depleting the blood of the amino acid asparagine, which is required for cells to survive. However, children eventually developed immunity to the drug and/

or suffered severe side effects that limited the use of asparaginase. In addition to prolonging the effective life of a drug, PEGlyation also helped to shield proteins from the human immune system so children would not experience severe side effects. There was significant risk in modifying asparaginase and reintroducing it into children known to have a severe reaction to it, but PEGylated asparaginase was successful and many of the children experienced remission of their leukemia. PEGylated asparaginase under the brand name Oncaspar® is still used as part of a treatment regimen for certain people with acute lymphoblastic leukemia.

Abe believed his technology could be used on many injectable and intravenous drugs, it became a big hit when it was successfully used on Interferon, which became a standard treatment for hepatitis. But his stockholders didn't have as much vision and patience as Abe did, and he was moved out of the company because they were not earning enough profits as quickly as the investors would like, and as big as they wanted. When Abe left Enzon, we no longer administered the free drug program for Adagen.

After a few years PEG-ADA was sold to another company that was interested in orphan drugs; an Italian drug company named Sigma-Tau Pharmaceuticals. Sigma-Tau still manufactures the drug under the brand name Adagen.

Abe was a character. He owned his own helicopter so he could fly to meetings when needed. He was ahead of his time in terms of technology; he felt he could not be separated from a telephone so he carried a heavy bulky portable phone attached to a battery almost the size of a car battery. It may have been a satellite phone, but he was never without it. This was years before cell phones became commonplace.

A few years after Abe left Enzon, he called to let me know he was starting another biotechnology company, and he intended to focus on orphan drugs. "Once those orphans get into your system," he said, "it's hard to get rid of them." I knew exactly what he meant.

*

Dr. Saul Brusilow of Johns Hopkins School of Medicine was a genius. No one ever doubted that. But he could also be a very disagreeable person. He had spent the bulk of his professional life studying a series of inherited metabolic diseases that were grouped under the title, "Urea Cycle Disorders." This group of metabolic disorders is characterized by deficiency of one of the enzymes of the "urea cycle," the process by which the body breaks down and removes nitrogen. Individuals with a urea cycle disorder cannot breakdown nitrogen, which (in the form of ammonia) accumulates in the blood.

Dr. Brusilow became the world's leading expert on these diseases. Although there are some dietary measures that can help (e.g., avoiding certain foods), periodically children would suffer an "attack" causing too much ammonia to accumulate in the blood. Most people know what ammonia can do to the skin if you use ammonia for cleaning purposes, but just imagine what it can do to the brain when ammonia tainted blood reaches the central nervous system.

Dr. Brusilow discovered the process that allows the body to make ammonia and dispose of it, so he developed a treatment in his lab to stop these children from suffering brain damage and death. Every child in the world diagnosed with a urea cycle disorder needed that medicine, but no company would manufacture it. Doctors would call him from South America, Europe and Asia to get the medicine for one of their patients, and they never knew if Dr. Brusilow would respond pleasantly or unpleasantly. But they had no choice; if they had a patient with a urea cycle disease they had to deal with Dr. Brusilow in order to obtain the needed medicine.

Dr. Brusilow's Johns Hopkins colleagues complained that his laboratory concoctions were smelling up the school. So the administration moved his laboratory to the basement, where it stayed for several years. He complained to everyone who would listen including me that he needed to find a pharmaceutical company willing to manufacture his drug, but no one was interested. I called a few companies to ask them to adopt Dr. Brusilow's drug (generic name: sodium phenylbuterate), they seemed interested for a few weeks until Dr. Brusilow said something to turn them off. What could that be? I could not figure out what he was doing to make them walk away, until one day Dr. Brusilow announced that he was starting his own pharmaceutical company.

Dr. Brusilow named his company Ucyclyd. It was impossible to spell or pronounce, but he had a monopoly on the urea cycle market throughout the world so he could name his company anything he wanted to. In 1996, when his drug, under the brand name Buphenyl®, was finally approved as an orphan drug for the American market, all 350 urea cycle patients in North America were taking the drug because there was no other treatment option. Upon approval, it was estimated that Buphenyl would cost $50,000 a year for an average patient. It was promised that the price would decrease as more patients survived and prescriptions were increased. Yet, the price continued to slowly escalate. The dosage was based partly on weight, so as a child grew older, the cost would rise for the individual family. Parents were up in arms but they couldn't do anything about it.

To calm them down I went with Dr. Marlene Haffner, Director of FDA's Office for Orphan Products Development, to visit leaders of the Urea Cycle support group. I couldn't blame them for being upset at the huge cost of the drug. After all, they were getting the drug for free from Dr. Brusilow for many years. It would have been a shock if he charged anything over $1,000 for the medicine, but $50,000 a year on average was not within their reality parameters. Marlene and I left that meeting wondering if we did any good at all, but at least we showed that we cared.

NORD ran a MAP program for Buphenyl; it only had 3 or 4 patients in it because the MAP was for uninsured patients, most of these patients were insured or on Medicaid. For these patients we administered a "co-pay fund" which covered their deductibles and co-pay fees if their family could not afford them.

The unfortunate truth is we couldn't do anything at all about drug prices. The only thing that lowers the cost of medicines in America is competition from generic drugs, and it would be at least seven more years before competition would be allowed on Buphenyl. In the case of biologics, the United States Congress had not yet enacted a law enabling FDA to approve generic copies of biologics. But Buphenyl was a chemical pharmaceutical, not a biologic. Sensing that he was not a good businessman Dr. Brusilow took on a partner, Norb Wiech, Ph.D., who managed the Ucyclyd business. Norb was an easy going person, but after a while he and Dr. Brusilow couldn't get along, the company was finally sold to Medicis Pharmaceutical in April of 1999. Medicis was a small new company based in Arizona, and in 2012 was acquired by a Canadian company called Valeant Pharmaceuticals. In 2013, Valeant sold the global rights to Buphenyl to a California company called Hyperion Therapeutics. By this point, the upper end cost of Buphenyl had reached $240,000 per year.

In 2014, the FDA approved Ravicti® for the treatment of certain urea cycle disorders in individuals 2 years of age and older. Ravacti is manufactured and marketed by Hyperion Therapeutics. The drug was approved under the Orphan Drug Act as an improvement over Buphenyl. The estimated cost – roughly $315,000 per year!

It has always been my fear that when a scientific genius like Saul Brusilow dies, the formula for his treatment will die with him unless he passes it on. When only one doctor is an expert on a rare disease, if he discovers a treatment he needs to share the formula. Otherwise, all of his patients will have to die with him. But in this case, Dr. Brusilow created a company, and the company owned the formula, so the drug will continue to be available long after the doctor is gone. Dr. Brusilow is about 85 years old now and he still lives in Maryland. Norb Wiech, on the other hand, went on to found another orphan drug company, Lysomics, Inc. Once orphan drugs get into your system, they just can't be ignored.

*

Usually, orphan drug advances are the product of time and effort over many years, but occasionally such advances happened quite quickly. A California ophthalmologist was treating an eye disease that involved muscles. One of these was a rare form of dystonia, a group of neurological diseases that involve painful involuntary muscle spasms. Benign essential blepharospasm (BEB) is a subtype of dystonia that is characterized by eyelids that do not open and close upon command. Eventually the patient becomes functionally blind because their eyelids stay closed unless the patient can hold their eyelids up with their fingers.

The ophthalmologist, Dr. Alan Scott, thought of ways he could paralyze muscles, he realized that botulism toxin does exactly that. People who get botulism through tainted food find their muscles become paralyzed. So he grew a small amount of botulism and drew off some toxin to inject into his patient with BEB. It worked and her eyes were no longer clamped shut. Even more astonishing the treatment lasted about 3 months, making injections necessary about four times a year, AND there was no effect on muscles outside of the injected areas.

Eventually he tried it on other forms of dystonia by injecting the spastic muscles wherever they occurred. For example, there is one form of dystonia (spasmodic torticollis) that affects neck muscles, it pulls the head over to one shoulder; spasmodic dysphonia puts the vocal chords into spasm and affects the voice, etc. He found that many forms of dystonia could be helped with a quarterly injection of botulinum toxin.

The doctor's wife, who was a dermatologist, marveled at the new treatment but she also noticed that wherever it was injected on the face, wrinkles disappeared!

No drug manufacturer was willing to grow botulism in their factory. At a meeting in Washington I met a man who worked for Allergan, a company well known for manufacturing over-the-counter contact lens solutions. I told him about Dr. Scott and the treatment for benign essential blepharospasm which also worked on lazy eye disease (a common childhood condition when the muscle of one eye is not as strong as the other eye). I asked him to contact Dr. Scott, and eventually Allergan became the sponsor of Botox (the brand name for botulinum toxin). Today Botox is approved for treatment of many orphan diseases involving spastic muscles, and as a bonus it is widely used for erasing wrinkles (not an orphan indication).

Botox became a blockbuster drug, only because an effort to help people with a very rare disease turned out to have benefits for a common cosmetic complaint!

*

Because of the success stories of orphan drugs such as botulinum toxin, thalidomide, human growth hormone, interferon, etc., the large multi-national pharmaceutical companies began to pay attention. In some cases they simply looked at the numbers – how could a treatment for fewer than 200,000 people in the U.S. be earning over one billion dollars per year in sales? How come one-third of all orphan drugs approved each year are for rare cancers? And how come out of all new drugs and biologics approved by the FDA each year, one-quarter to one-third of them are consistently orphan drugs? They started to reason that instead of ignoring possible treatments for rare health conditions maybe they should take a second look at those drugs in the context of the Orphan Drug Act.

It took some time, but eventually they realized that the pharmaceutical market had changed and the size of a market was no longer as important as attacking a serious disease that has no other treatment options: orphan drugs for rare disorders!

Chapter 12

Working with
the Government

"As I hurtled through space, one thought kept crossing my mind —
every part of this rocket was supplied by the lowest bidder."

John Glenn, Astronaut and U.S. Senator

Ever since President Ronald Reagan proclaimed that the federal
government was not the answer, indeed "Government is the
problem" he insisted, many conservative U.S. citizens have felt that
they should not owe anything for the rights and privileges of living
in the United States, except perhaps raising the American flag on
certain holidays and singing the national anthem at sports events.

Jerry and I have always felt differently, he spent over seven years in
the United States Army. After we groan appropriately around tax
time but we know that the price of our citizenship is the annual
federal income tax, so we pay it. When called for jury duty, we always
turn up at the local court house on time and neatly dressed. Even
though in retirement, we have no young children, we never refuse to
pay school taxes, because that's what we owe to the next generation.

Every generation stands on the shoulders of previous generations and we are born indebted to them.

Therefore, when the federal government has asked me to serve on federal committees and commissions, even though I often knew such service could be painfully boring and time-consuming, I never refused. It is the price that one must pay for the freedoms that we enjoy and sometimes, I learned more from the meetings than the knowledge I was able to contribute. Those meetings were the price I had to pay for the privilege of freely complaining about my government.

*

The first government group I was asked to serve on was the Department of Health and Human Services' (HHS) *National Commission on Orphan Diseases* (1986-89). The Commission was mandated by a section of the Orphan Drug Act, but it took three years before HHS fully implemented the mandate. Membership of the Commission was proscribed by the law, thus, 10 members were research scientists from various institutions and five came from various other backgrounds. I served as a consumer advocate representing patients, their families and rare disease support groups. Some representatives of the pharmaceutical industry voluntarily attended the meetings as non-voting members. I remember doctors George Goldstein and Larry Weaver attending some meetings. Formal meetings of the Commission were scheduled around the country so we could get input from families, patients, drug companies, researchers and medical professionals from different geographic areas.

Steve Groft served as the Executive Secretary of the Commission and was responsible for writing the Commission's final report with recommendations to Congress. This was not an easy task because 15 Commission members expressed 15 points of view, compromises had to be made. The Commission's final report comprised several volumes resembling telephone-book size and thickness. The first two years of the Commission were chaired by a woman, Glenna Crooks, Ph.D., who was a consultant to drug companies. Unfortunately, the fact that a pharmaceutical industry person was Chairing the Commission undermined consumer s' and politician s' trust that the final report would validate the needs of patients. Glenna, who was a very smart and genuinely nice person, resigned the Chairmanship after two years because she sensed the final report summarizing the three years of information gathered should be chaired by an academic scientist. Dr. Jess Thoene, from the University of Michigan, became the new Chairman for the last year and his name is on the final report to Congress.

I remember two significant things about the Commission meetings. The first is an incident that occurred when leaders of rare disease support groups were asked to testify about their perceptions of the obstacles to research advancements and new therapies. At this particular meeting, the mother of a child with a rare disease testified that she didn't want her daughter to participate in any clinical trials. She felt since not much would be known about an experimental drug, she would not want her daughter "to be the guinea pig." Thus she would wait until the drug was approved for sale in the United States.

I waited for her to finish her testimony, which basically was a litany of complaints that too little was known about the disease and not enough scientists were studying the disease, etc. I simply thanked her for coming and testifying today, "but if you are not willing to have your daughter participate in a clinical trial, whose daughter should participate in that research?" She looked at me strangely because she was surprised at the question, she had no answer.

The dumbfounded mother was thinking in terms of common diseases – "let someone else's child go into those tests for sore throat remedies and then my child will benefit from that knowledge without experiencing any perils." But her daughter did not have a sore throat, afflicting millions of children who could be used as test subjects. She had a disease affecting only 300 to 500 children in the United States, meaning if her daughter would not participate in one of three separate and distinct phases of clinical tests (phase I, phase II and finally phase III), whose child would willingly be sacrificed on the altar? When you have a rare disease you cannot sit back and say, "Let someone else be the guinea pig." If not your child, then whose? I stayed in touch with that mother for many years because she started a support group and needed to learn the realities of how to encourage medical research. Scientists don't wake up one morning and decide to pursue research on an under-studied malady with small patient populations. They know that it will be much easier to get funding to study prevalent diseases because families keep pressure on Congress to adequately fund cancer research, stroke, Alzheimer's disease, diabetes, etc. But no one pressures their Congressman for more funding of research on Stevens-Johnson syndrome, Stiff person syndrome, epidermolysis bullosa or the thousands of rare diseases that remain underfunded and under-researched.

In general, disease support groups need to raise money for research on their disease and ultimately fund small research grants for academic scientists to study the disease. If any of those research projects reveal important information, the scientist could use the data to apply for a larger grant from the NIH, a large foundation that funds research or a company in the business of bringing new treatments or diagnostics to market. That is the way disease support groups attract researchers to their disease and it all starts with fund raising. But fund raising is difficult for unfamiliar diseases that people can't pronounce or even spell, support group leaders are usually volunteers who have no training in fund raising.

Such problems seem to be insurmountable, except if you have a loved one with the disease. Somehow people involved in support groups find an inner strength that enables them to overcome adversity for the sake of their child, their spouse, their parent, their brother or sister or their loved one. Very often they befriend people from other disease support groups and learn from their failures and successes in the business of "charities."

*

The second thing that I remember from my days on the Commission was an incident that occurred years before, when I started working at the Tourette Syndrome Association. Everyone was complaining that there was no research on TS. I asked the research doctors why they thought there was no federally funded research and they answered, "Everyone knows you can't get NIH to fund a research grant on a rare disease like TS."

I made an appointment at the National Institute of Health (NIH) with the Director of the National Institute for Neurological and Communicative Disorders and Stroke* (NINCDS). (*the title of this Institute was subsequently changed to the National Institute for Neurological Disorders and Stroke [NINDS], while responsibility for research on communicative disorders was transferred to the new National Institute for Deafness and Other Communication Disorders [NIDCD]).

When I visited the neurology institute at the huge NIH campus in Bethesda, Maryland, two or three other Board members from the TSA accompanied me and we unloaded our frustration at the Director. No federal funding was spent on TS research and we wanted to know why. "I'll tell you why," the Director calmly said. "No one has applied for a TS research grant."

"That's impossible," we said in unison. The neurological researchers had told us that it's impossible to get funding for a research grant on TS. How would they know that if they had not been denied funding on a TS grant application?

"Well," said the Director. "That may be what they're telling each other but we have not received a TS grant application here for many years. So I don't know how they know it would not be funded." I don't know how other attendees felt, but I was embarrassed. We were there to lobby the Director about an apparently imaginary problem.

When we got back to New York the leaders of the TSA had a big job to do. They had to educate research scientists and urge them to apply for NIH grants to study TS. We had to monitor their grant applications and if they were not funded we needed to find out why (if the researcher was willing to tell us). And most importantly we created a "seed money grant program" to fund small research grants. "Seed money" grants were ample to provide researchers with enough resources to leverage an idea and gather enough proof to show the need for further study. The small grants enabled scientists to gather just enough data and show the need for a larger federally funded research grant. That job required a full time staff person, Sue Levi-Pearl, who subsequently launched an international cooperative study on the genetics of TS.

When I was a member of the Commission, we were sitting around a table one day and the ten research scientists began commiserating about the NIH's reluctance to fund research grants on rare diseases, I told them about my experience at the neurological institute and the embarrassment I felt when I learned that no scientist had applied for a research grant on Tourette syndrome in many years. I warned them not to make a statement in the report that would be proven wrong. Thus they agreed to send questions to the NIH that would document how much rare disease research was being funded by the government. We quickly learned it was not sufficient to limit those questions to NIH because many other divisions of government shared responsibility for medical research such as the Veteran's Administration (VA), the Centers for Disease Control (CDC), Department of Defense (DoD), and many more government agencies.

*

Unfortunately, the main problem with the Commission's report was that, despite making many recommendations, Congress did not implement most of them primarily because they would cost money. However, one recommendation was granted: The Commission recommended that NIH should create an "Office for Rare Diseases" to coordinate rare disease research throughout all of the Institutes.

For example, until that time a grant application to study TS would sometimes be sent to the institute responsible for neurology research (NINCDS) or the institute responsible for research on mental health (NIMH) or the institute responsible for research on children and pregnant women (NICHD) or the institute responsible for general medical research known as the National Institute for General Medicine Sciences (NIGMS). NIGMS was responsible for genetic research until the NIH finally created the Human Genome Project and a separate institute known as the National Human Genome Research Institute (NHGRI) for the study of genetic science.

There was usually no specific reason for sending a grant application to a specific institute unless the applicant asked for it to be specifically routed to one institute. Thus applying for an NIH grant could be as predictable as a craps shoot… a researcher could not predict which institute their application would be routed to and whether any grant reviewers would know anything about the disease they wanted to study!

The person most responsible for expanding the role of NIH after WW II was the great philanthropist and health advocate, Mary Lasker. She objected to the formation of an institute devoted to "general medical sciences" because she noted, "No one ever dies of general medicine." This statement rightly implied that the NIGM would not have a natural constituency to lobby Congress for its funding. Mary Lasker was the first lay person to understand the politics of medical research funding; health advocates today owe her a great debt for passing much of that knowledge on to us.

Mary Woodard Lasker was a brilliant and charming woman who married a very wealthy man, Albert Lasker. She was raised in Watertown Wisconsin by an upper middle class family. She graduated from Radcliffe College in 1923 with a degree in art history and married an art dealer in 1926. The marriage was not successful and they divorced in 1934.

Health activism became a part of Mary's life as early as 1938 when she joined the Birth Control Federation, which later became the Planned Parenthood Federation. She was 38 years old when she met Albert David Lasker (1880-1952), a wealthy advertising pioneer who made a fortune creating distinctive brands. He was impressed with Mary's business acumen, her love of art, and her passion for improving public health. They married in 1940.

Albert Lasker sold his advertising firm in 1942 and the couple devoted themselves to making health insurance widely available and promoting medical research that would lead to more treatments, preventive measures and cures. Mary used Albert Lasker's knowledge and connections to high government leaders and lobbied them for more funds in support of medical research. It was around that time, in 1942, that they created the Albert and Mary Lasker Foundation to provide awards to researchers who made major medical discoveries and disease advancements.

Albert died of cancer in 1952. As a child, Mary had witnessed profound suffering of a family friend who died of breast cancer. She could never forget the suffering she witnessed and, after her husband died, she swore to fight cancer for the rest of her life. She educated herself by talking to as many cancer doctors and researchers as possible. Among other things, she helped create and promote the American Cancer Society, but she felt only the federal government had enough power and resources to find a cure for cancer. She used her various contacts in the elite political world to convince Congress to create the National Cancer Institute (NCI). In the 2 years following WW II, the federal government's support of biomedical research rose from $3 million to $1 billion because of Mary Lasker's advocacy.

Mary Lasker was instrumental in helping Lyndon Johnson to pass Medicare and Medicaid legislation. She also helped Richard Nixon launch his "war on cancer", but when new cures failed to materialize politicians used it as proof that you can't throw money at problems and expect them to disappear. But by that time her example had taught many other disease groups and professional medical society's how to lobby for increased research funding. Lasker is credited with creating a powerful American research lobby, the largest medical research enterprise in the world (the NIH), and elevating the importance of medical research on the nation's annual agenda.

*

When the Office of Rare Diseases (ORD), now known as the Office of Rare Disease Research (ORDR), was ultimately created at NIH in 1993, Steven Groft was named its Director. Finally, rare disease research would have a home at NIH, and would benefit from the extraordinary experience and knowledge that Steve and his staff (especially his 2nd in command staffer, Henrietta Hyatt-Knorr) had nurtured throughout his career. For example, Steve kept track of funding difficulties at all NIH institutes, so he could negotiate deals among several institutes which enabled them to co-fund a grant that may have been too expensive for one institute to support. His office also supported international meetings focused on little known diseases, with a goal of getting other researchers interested. And eventually he and Dr. William (Bill) Gahl convinced NIH to create a sorely needed program for "Undiagnosed Diseases" where people with no diagnosis could go with the hope of obtaining a name for their medical condition. Dr. Gahl runs the clinic, and word got out quickly about the pioneering efforts of the NIH medical staff in the "undiagnosed program" who ultimately found new diseases that had not been characterized before.

In some cases, NIH clinicians were able to diagnose these patients with existing diseases that were unfamiliar to the patients' doctors and in other cases, after extensive genetic analyses, new diseases were identified and characterized so they could be added to the medical literature. Within a year there were so many applicants begging to be evaluated at NIH's undiagnosed disease clinic that waiting lists became the norm.

*

In 1995, I joined the FDA's Biological Response Modifiers Advisory Committee (BRMAC), where I served until 1999. After my term was over I was called back various times over the next 5 years to temporarily cover the mandatory "consumer" seat on this FDA Advisory Panel.

Like most government agencies, names of divisions or departments can be impossible to spell, pronounce or understand! The FDA is especially complicated because they use so much medical terminology. But why they named something a "biological response modifier" is beyond comprehension. Even scientists don't appear to understand it.

An FDA staff person once told me that the agency was unprepared for the upsurge of biotechnology products in the 1980s and 90s. Until the early 1990s, the agency's structure for regulating medicines was simply a division for drugs and another division to regulate "biologics." Until then biologics were made from human or animal products, mostly blood and plasma.

But biotechnology changed everything because scientists found ways to manufacture enzymes, proteins and other biological products by growing them in huge vats. They were able to implant a gene into a bacterium or an animal ovary cell, etc., making the bacterium or cell into a mini-factory that churned out large quantities of the needed product. For example, insulin for diabetics used to be taken from cows or pigs but biotechnology enabled companies to grow insulin in huge vats without having to worry if the cow or pig may have had a disease that could make the human sick. During the 1990s companies stopped making animal insulin and henceforth all insulin in the industrialized world was manufactured through biotechnology.

The FDA created the BRMAC to oversee some of the new biotechnology products like interferon and interleukin, which are products that the human body manufactures in very small quantities, but that biotechnology factories churned out in large quantities. Both of these medicines (the interferons and interleukins) were found to have properties affecting the immune system, which meant they could fight diseases such as hepatitis or boost the immune system to fight cancer.

Having already served on the Recombinant DNA Advisory Committee (RAC) at NIH, I knew I was facing another steep learning curve at the BRMAC. But in a short time I came to understand the reason why one seat on the committee was reserved for a consumer representative. The scientists could debate a scientific point until their face turned blue, and sometimes no one was thinking about the impact on patients. Someone had to remind them to think "what do patients need?" and "how will this medicine help patients?"

The audience at BRMAC meetings were mostly Wall Street investment firms, newspaper and magazine writers and drug companies that wanted to learn what their competitors were doing. Since the public didn't know very much about biotechnology, it was a good venue to teach the public that biotechnology was nothing to worry about and it was actually helping mankind by providing large quantities of precious medicines.

*

There were several issues that I will never forget from the meetings of the BRMAC: The discovery of endogenous viruses in pig tissue, pancreas tissue transplants, and the mysteries of Mad Cow disease. This is not to say that many other topics we reviewed during the almost ten years of my service on the BRMAC (1995-2005) were uninteresting. It is simply that these topics were so extraordinarily different that there were no historical theories, experiments or precedents to base an opinion on.

The issue of pig viruses arose only because a biotech company decided to genetically modify pigs with the hope that their inner organs could be transplanted in humans.

In the early 1980s, several drugs reached the market that could tame the immune system's response to organ transplants. Because these drugs protected transplanted organs and improved success rates, the lists of people who needed organ transplants grew longer every year. But there were an insufficient number of people who agreed to become organ donors either while they were alive, or after they died. Thousands of kidneys, hearts, livers and other organs were desperately needed, but even when a person willingly signed up to become an organ donor, the last minute wishes of their family could veto the dead person's wishes. However, the greatest number of organs was lost when doctors did not know what the wishes of a dying person were, and if no close relative was available at the death to make a decision, doctors assumed that the person did not wish to donate their organs. Therefore the number of organs available for transplantation in the United States has never reached its potential. Scientists had long known that the tissues of pigs are closely related to human tissues. For many years physicians had used heart valves from pigs to replace the valves in human hearts, without serious signs of rejection. But replacing a human kidney or liver with a kidney or liver from a pig was not yet possible because the human immune system recognized the new organ as a foreign body that needed to be rejected from the human patient.

Some scientists were convinced that that genetic manipulation of the pig genome could create porcine organs for transplantation in humans. They created a biotechnology company that raised the genetically modified pigs so their organs could be harvested. Then they came before the BRMAC to see whether the organs could be approved for sale, and if not, why not. The implication for many products that were denied marketing approval was that "more studies are needed" before the FDA's questions could be adequately answered.

But a few months before the BRMAC meeting a startling discovery about pigs had been made. Apparently, viruses that had entered pig genomes thousands of years ago had been camouflaged and inherited by the next generation, one pig generation after another for thousands of years. There was no known ways to get the viruses out of pig's cells, so humans could probably become infected with the viruses through transplanted organs from pigs.

Were the viruses dangerous? Apparently they were not dangerous to pigs but no one knew if they would be dangerous to humans. If humans were given transplanted organs from pigs, they would have to take immune-moderating drugs to prevent organ rejection. Would those transplant drugs awaken the viruses in the pig organs? Would the drugs prevent the organ recipient's immune system from fighting off an infection from the unfamiliar virus?

No one could answer these questions. But the topic was fascinating enough to the scientific community that they wondered if other animals had inherited endogenous viruses in their genomes. The answer was yes, other types of animals have inherited viruses from many past generations. Do humans also have viruses hidden in their genome? No one knew the answer.

Therefore, the company breeding pigs for organ transplantation was not able to put the organs on the American market because the BRMAC voted "no". However some scientists are still trying to find ways to rid animal cells of inherited viruses. Until then, mankind is likely to continue suffering from shortages of organs for transplantation.

*

After my official term was finished on the BRMAC, the FDA would contact me from time to time when they needed a consumer representative to sit in on a particular meeting. I remember a particularly poignant meeting that reviewed transplantation of certain pancreatic tissues in people with very serious type 1-diabetes. There are two types of diabetes: type-1 is believed to be an autoimmune disease in which the human immune system destroys insulin-making tissues in the pancreas. This type of diabetes usually affects people during childhood and lasts throughout life. Because the body cannot manufacture enough insulin, type-1 diabetics have to take insulin injections, or it can be infused through implanted insulin pumps or pods. A low carbohydrate diet is also needed to avoid high blood sugar.

Type-2 diabetes is much more common than type-1. Millions of people come down with type-2 diabetes, usually in adulthood after the age of 50. In type-2 diabetes the body usually can still manufacture some insulin, but the cells do not use insulin properly, which is called "insulin resistance." At first, the body tends to make more and more insulin in an effort to keep blood sugar at a normal level. But after a while, the body can't make enough insulin, causing blood sugar to rise. Medications and/ or insulin, along with diet, are needed to keep blood sugar near the normal level to avoid the long-term consequences of diabetes (e.g., blindness, loss of toes or limb, etc.).

When the BRMAC staff called me to ask me to go to this meeting I was interested because I have type-2 diabetes, thus anything I could do to help find improved treatments would be worthwhile. I had gotten diabetes during all three of my pregnancies (gestational diabetes), but it would go away a few days after the baby was born. However, a doctor had warned me not to be fooled by the temporary nature of gestational diabetes. "It will come back full force when you're around age 50," he warned, "so stay on a low carbohydrate diet forever with hope of delaying permanent diabetes as long as possible."

He was correct. Diabetes came back full force when I was in my 50s. For a few years diet and oral medications were helpful, but when I retired, I was switched to insulin injections.

At the BRMAC meeting I learned that pancreas transplants have been used for people with severe type-1 diabetes for some time, but there are not enough pancreas organs available to treat all the people who need them. Additionally, even when the pancreas transplant was helpful, the immune system of the type-1 diabetic patient would destroy the insulin-making cells, so another transplant would eventually be needed. Some American and Canadian doctors wondered, if instead of transplanting an entire pancreas, would transplanting only some insulin-making cells from a healthy pancreas be sufficient? There are so many insulin making cells in a pancreas, it may be possible to transplant the cells into a number of diabetics, rather than one pancreas into one diabetic.

They tried it and it worked. After the scientists made their presentations, the floor was opened to people in the audience. This was obviously a very important hearing for type-1 diabetics because there were several of them in the audience and they wanted to speak.

As each person came to the microphone they asked the committee to approve the pancreas cell transplants because to them it meant the difference between life and death. They talked about having out-of-control high blood sugars, which they tested several times a day. They also spoke about low blood sugars, which can be life threatening events. For any diabetic when the signs of low blood sugar appear (shaking, sweating, etc.) they need immediate infusion of sugar or carbohydrate foods to bring their blood sugar levels up quickly (e.g., orange juice, candy, sweet soda, raisins, etc.). The patients compared the horror of their lives before the transplant and the relief after the transplant. Some said they were able to go off insulin after the pancreas cell transplant but others said they were still taking insulin but at a greatly reduced dosage.

When we broke for lunch I decided to have a private chat with some of the women, especially because a few of them used the magic word, "Cure." I told them I was a type-2 diabetic so I was very interested in their experiences. But even those who told the most miraculous stories at the microphone, claiming that they were "cured" of diabetes, admitted that as time went on the diabetes came back and practically all of them were back on insulin.

Thinking about this throughout the day, I wondered how come those patients didn't realize that they weren't "cured", and that the same destructive process that caused them to lose their insulin producing cells in the first place was destroying the transplanted cells just as efficiently now. If the FDA approved the process, would it be worthwhile to put other diabetics through the surgery knowing the therapeutic effect would not last? And should they be exposed to transplant drugs that would lower their immune system, even though diabetics already have problems fighting off infections?

After the lunch break members of the committee were allowed to ask questions and the doctors on the committee had plenty of questions. But I asked the last question. I said when I sit on an FDA Advisory Committee we usually review a product – a drug, a medical device, or even a diagnostic test, etc. But it appeared there was no product that the presenters wanted to manufacture or sell. Transplanting cells is a procedure, not a product. So I asked them to tell me what product they wanted to see approved for the American market.

After a lot of head scratching one of the patients in the audience said, "If the FDA doesn't approve this, our insurance won't pay for it." But the FDA is not in the business of approving a surgical practice. The FDA does not regulate organ transplants, but it does regulate the drugs used to store and transport donated organs, and drugs that patients have to take to prevent rejection of the transplanted organ, or even the instruments used in the operating room, but NOT the transplant procedure itself.

As I remember that meeting, the committee did not take a vote at the end of the meeting because there was no product for us to approve or deny. The problem of insurance reimbursement is indeed profound, but it is not the FDA's role to approve a surgical procedure. I don't know which department of government would have that responsibility except to say if Medicare will pay for a procedure, insurance companies will usually, but not always, follow Medicare. Nevertheless, the inability of the committee to satisfy the patients in the audience still haunts me.

*

When I found out that the BRMAC was going to review Mad Cow disease, I was excited. Before cows came into the picture the disease was known as Creutzfeld-Jakob disease (CJD) and it was one of the most mysterious and rarest diseases known to science, with only one person in one million affected. That is because CJD is an infection caused not by bacteria, not by a virus, not by a fungus or parasite, but by a "prion."

A "prion" is a misfolded, infectious protein. When it enters a cell, it converts properly folded proteins into a misfolded state. No one understands why or how this occurs. However, in most prion diseases, it takes many years for the invading prion to hijack enough proteins to destroy the brain.

Prions were first discovered in the Fore tribe of New Guinea. There was an epidemic in the tribe that was recognized during the 1950s and 1960s. American scientists were sent to study the tribe and define the disease that was killing them. They named the disease "Kuru." Over a period of many decades members of the tribe became neurologically impaired; they lost coordination and balance, shivered, developed dementia and ultimately died.

By living with the tribe the scientists discovered that, when a relative died, the family performed a ritualistic cannibalism and family members consumed the brain tissue of their dead relative. Prions destroy human brains, and they are highly infectious. They can be transmitted not only by eating, but by touching open sores or wounds of an infected person or animal.

A medical journal article by Dr. Stanley Prusiner, published in 1982, coined the term "prion," which combined the words "protein" and "infection." Today there are no more cases of "Kuru" in New Guinea because the tribe learned not to eat human remains. But bovine spongiform encephalopathy occurs in cattle and is popularly known as "Mad Cow disease" in Europe and the Americas. In sheep and goats the disease is known as "Scrapie" and in deer and elk it is known as "Chronic Wasting Disease." The meat of animals that die of prion diseases must not be eaten because it contains prions that can cause Creutzfeld-Jakob disease or "fatal familial insomnia" in humans, and likely other human diseases that will probably be discovered in the future. All prion diseases are fatal because there is no treatment to destroy prions. To many in the scientific world, the discovery of prions was met with skepticism. However, in 1997, Stanley Prusiner won the Nobel Prize in Physiology or Medicine for the discovery of prions, which at the time were a new disease-causing agent.

The BRMAC listened to presentations by many experts who were knowledgeable about prion diseases. A number of cases had occurred in Great Britain in recent years, which raised alarms throughout Europe and North America. It was discovered that some bovine feed had apparently been contaminated by ground up sheep that had died of Scrapie, which had been sprinkled into the food that was sold as cow and cattle feed. Thus the prions from the sheep were fed to cows and cattle, and the beef from those animals was eaten by humans who died.

Once the cause was identified government rules were changed to prevent farmers from feeding products that contain animal tissues to other animals. Eventually a few other cases of prion diseases occurred in other European countries and Canada. In the United States there were three or four cases occurring in people who had lived at some time in Europe, and one or two cows were identified with Mad Cow disease. But American law had never allowed the mixing of animal food with dead animal products so the animals had to have gotten the disease from some other source.

Unfortunately, because of my position at NORD, I would hear from people whose loved ones were diagnosed with Creutzfeld-Jakob disease. They were always mystified about where their loved one could have contracted a prion disease. But I always asked them, "Was he a hunter?", because in recent years contaminated deer and elk have been an important source of prion disease in the United States. These wild animals live in the lush forests of North America and Chronic Wasting Disease has been documented in these herds for more than a decade. They are not fed commercial farm food, so it is a mystery how they are contracting the disease. I have faith that someday scientists will figure it all out.

I served on the committee that heard testimony about prion diseases, including the known sources of contamination, but no one had any suggestions about possible treatments. After the cases in Great Britain occurred, the government banned any animal feed that contained ingredients that could contain prions. When cases of "Mad Cow Disease" stopped occurring in Europe, there was no more urgency to study the problem and find a treatment. In the absence of urgency a disease is usually ignored, and it stays ignored until it raises its ugly head and occurs anew.

Chapter 13

The Rise, Fall and Rebirth of Gene Therapy

"Yesterday is not ours to recover, but tomorrow is ours to win or lose."

Lyndon Johnson, 36ᵗʰ American President

My time on the NIH *Human Gene Therapy Sub-Committee* deserves special note. I served on the committee from 1989 to 1992. During this time, gene therapy was being hailed as the next major breakthrough medical technology that would conquer disease according to Wall Street and Hollywood. Unlike various treatments for genetic diseases, gene therapy was going *"cure"* children with genetic diseases whether it was muscular dystrophy or cystic fibrosis or sickle cell anemia.

However, when I joined this subcommittee the experiments had been limited to laboratory beakers, mice and a few monkeys. The subcommittee was under the larger Recombinant DNA Advisory Committee (known as "the RAC"). The RAC was responsible for reviewing most of the new scientific technologies related to medicine. But RAC members needed guidance from more experts familiar with gene therapy in the laboratory, animals and in humans.

Apparently the RAC had realized that gene therapy was almost ready for human testing, so they wanted the newly formed sub-committee in place before the first human clinical trials could be approved or disapproved. All human gene therapy trials in the United States, when any federal funds were involved, were required to go through the sub-committee and then get the permission of the RAC before the first patient could be treated. So if the experiment was going to take place in a hospital, if the hospital accepted Medicare or Medicaid money, then federal funds were involved and RAC's permission was required. But if the actual experiment was funded entirely by private money, or if it took place outside of the United States, the RAC had no jurisdiction over the experiment.

I was no expert on anything related to science, so I had a long learning curve ahead of me. I knew, however, that just hanging around with scientists helped me to learn by osmosis; the knowledge would seep through my pores whether I wanted it to or not, and eventually I could understand what the scientists were talking about.

The first human gene therapy experiment that was close to human experimentation involved an NIH staff physician, W. French Anderson, M.D., who had also been dubbed "the father of gene therapy" by the popular press. Dr. Anderson was a physician and molecular biologist who graduated from Harvard Medical School in 1963. He spent most of his professional life working for the government at the NIH. It was generally believed that Dr. Anderson was the first to suggest that if scientists could get a functioning healthy gene into a person with a genetic disease (thus that person was assumed to have malfunctioning genes) that they could possibly cure the disease. However, a gene that is inserted directly into a cell does not usually function. So for years he worked on vectors, the "carriers" that would transport a therapeutic gene through the barriers of the body and ultimately deposit the healthy gene inside the target cells.

Anderson and other scientists decided that viruses would be good vectors. Viruses are used because they can infect the target cells. A virus is first modified so it can no longer cause disease. Then the virus is implanted with a healthy gene. The virus acts like a taxi, travels into a human cell and "drops-off" the healthy gene inside. Once the gene was efficiently transferred via a viral vector and tested on small animals in the lab, it would be time for human testing.

Years of laboratory work preceded human testing. They needed to find viruses that could be modified to no longer cause human disease, but nevertheless were able to penetrate human cells. They even looked at viruses that do cause human diseases, like cold viruses and even HIV viruses that cause AIDS, but they had to develop technology that could destroy the ability of those viruses to replicate and make people sick. Finally, Dr. Anderson searched for a disease that would be an appropriate testing ground, settling on a form of severe combined immune deficiency (aka the bubble boy disease) caused by a deficiency of the ADA enzyme (SCID-ADA). He reasoned that the disease was untreatable and fatal, it affected children, therefore, gene therapy would be the last hope for the survival of these children. But he did not know about Abe Abuchowski's development of the orphan drug, pegademase bovine (Adagen®) also known as PEG-ADA.

*

A few weeks before each subcommittee meeting, I would receive a huge box or several boxes of information that had to be read before the meeting. So I always walked into each meeting prepared to listen and ask questions. I was surprised to read that the sub-committee was going to consider Dr. Anderson's experiment on SCID-ADA in one of the first meetings I would attend.

I listened to the discussions of scientists on the committee who peppered Dr. Anderson with technical questions. They were so intensely technical that I knew I would fall asleep from boredom unless I found a way to keep my eyes open. There was always a large pad of paper in front of each participant so they could make notes, but I found out if I used the pad for drawing I could stay awake and patiently wait for all the technical issues to be exhausted. I settled on drawing flowers, which I did for years on many government committees, leaving the drawings for anyone who wanted them.

So after Dr. Anderson answered all of the technical questions I asked him why he chose SCID-ADA. He explained it was a deadly and untreatable genetic disease, so if gene therapy works it would be fantastic for families who otherwise had no hope. I told him I was surprised he had not heard that a few weeks before this meeting the FDA had approved an enzyme-replacement therapy for SCID-ADA, meaning it was finally a treatable disease. To obtain the FDA's approval the manufacturer had to prove that their treatment was both safe and effective. Thus SCID-ADA was no longer "untreatable."

Dr. Anderson admitted that he did not know that the orphan drug was approved by the FDA, but he did know that some of his potential research subjects were taking the drug. So I asked him if he intended to provide gene therapy to the children who continued to take Adagen, or if he intended to take them off the drug before infusing the gene therapy. He answered that he would take them off the drug.

I had to respond that since SCID-ADA is now a treatable disease it would be ethically irresponsible to require them to stop taking the enzyme. Would you ask a diabetic to stop taking insulin before you give that patient a new treatment? Bioethicists would demand that you continue to give them insulin and after adding the new drug, gradually withdraw the insulin. I asked Dr. Anderson to continue giving the children PEG-ADA, which is the "standard treatment" for the disease, and once he gets a signal that the gene therapy is working, gradually withdraw the drug.

Dr. Anderson was not happy with me. I could measure the annoyance in his eyes. But since the whole sub-committee agreed with me, he had no choice but to keep the children on the drug. No one at that table hoped as much as I that the gene therapy would work and the PEG-ADA could be withdrawn. But removing it before the gene therapy would be like telling the children to cross a canyon on tightrope without a safety net.

Another member of the sub-committee was Doris Zallen, Ph.D., a professor at Virginia Tech who specializes in bioethics with a focus on genetic ethics. It turned out that Doris and I were both brought up in Brooklyn, so we had a cultural background in common. We enjoyed talking because we knew where each of us was coming from, so I talked with Doris about the issue of enzyme replacement therapy for the SCID-ADA children. She agreed with me; the enzyme replacement therapy should only be withdrawn after there was evidence that the gene therapy was working successfully.

*

When Doris and I were young we had both been shocked to learn about a catastrophe at Willowbrook State School. The Willowbrook incident, along with other similarly horrendous human medical experiments such as the Tuskegee experiment, helped to raise public awareness about the burgeoning field of study known as "bioethics." Although bioethics traces its origins to the mid-1950s when a committee had to decide who would be able to use dialysis machines, the term gained prominence when Van Rensselaer Potter applied the term "bioethics" in 1970, just two years before the Tuskegee scandal became public. Society could no longer allow doctors and researchers to decide what is or is not ethical in medical experimentation.

Scientists are driven to find the answer to scientific questions, sometimes without concern for the welfare of patients, which can easily contradict the Hippocratic Oath. A scientist can reason that the temporary discomfort of a few people counterbalances the benefits of curing or preventing a disease that kills or cripples millions of people. Such decisions should not be in the hands of scientists alone. Eventually, American research institutions were required to have an "Institutional Review Board" (IRB), a committee of people which would review a proposed study and ensure that institutional personnel were following ethical standards. This arose after the public outrage to the Tuskegee scandal as part of the National Research Act of 1974.

This is why people who volunteer for medical experiments in the U.S. are given an "informed consent" document that they must read and sign, that document must explain all of the risks and possible benefits of participation in that experiment. In time, most of Europe and some Asian countries also converted to the "informed consent" doctrine.

*

Doris Zallen and I spent the next few years as the voices of patients on the NIH gene therapy committees; we tried to ensure that patients were told the truth about what was known and what was unknown about human gene therapy. But every time we objected to poorly written and even dishonest informed consent documents, some researchers in the room would roll their eyes. "Don't you understand," some researchers would insist, "researchers are not free to change the informed consent document. The final decisions about the final wording are made by hospital lawyers, not medical doctors. The only thing they care about in consent documents is whether the hospital's liability is adequately covered."

Despite Willowbrook, despite Tuskegee, despite the horrendous medical experiments in Nazi concentration camps, despite our collective conviction that "it could never happen here," it does happen here primarily because the informed consent document has degenerated into a document of protection against liability for hospitals and doctors. They too often do not fulfill their primary purpose of providing understandable and truthful information to patient volunteers, along with an honest assessment of whether a person may benefit from the knowledge gained, or whether they may not benefit and might even be harmed by the experiment. Every few years there are rumblings that something should be done to modernize and upgrade the American human protection system for biomedical research, but nothing is ever codified.

After serving on the NIH Human Gene Therapy Subcommittee from 1989 to 1992, I (along with Doris) was appointed to the NIH Recombinant DNA Advisory Committee (RAC) from 1993 to 1996. As members of the RAC Doris insisted that patient protection regulations for gene therapy experiments should be more specific and detailed, and that the NIH should specify exactly what the documents should contain. The RAC formed a committee for this purpose and Doris was appointed as the committee Chair. I became a member of the committee. Doris wrote a superb document of rules governing patient protections for people undergoing gene therapy experiments and the RAC voted to adopt the new rules.

Thereafter the RAC gave detailed instructions to scientists as to what must be contained in informed consent documents for gene therapy experiments. Those instructions had to be more comprehensive than other patient protection documents because the technology was new, we did not know what could possibly go wrong if the genes did not behave the way scientists expected, we were totally ignorant of whether gene therapy could possibly affect future generations if the patient went on to have children.

*

Sometime after the incident with Dr. Anderson on the gene therapy subcommittee, we were scheduled to have a NORD meeting in Washington DC, I knew that leaders of support groups and patients would want to hear about gene therapy from the "father of gene therapy." So I wrote to Dr. Anderson and asked if he would give a half-hour talk to the leaders of rare disease support groups. First he sent a negative reply to my invitation, but about a week later he changed his mind and said yes. I was very grateful.

When the day for Dr. Anderson's speech arrived I was listening to another speaker at the NORD meeting, when a staff person whispered to me that Dr. French Anderson was in the hallway and he wanted to speak to me before his presentation. So I went to greet him outside of the auditorium. "Dr. Anderson, thank you so much for coming," I said with my hand extended. But he did not take my hand. Instead he let out all the negative frustration and anger that he had withheld at the subcommittee meeting.

"Do you realize, Mrs. Meyers, that I have spent a large part of my professional life studying and developing gene therapy until I am almost at the goal, and you are apparently determined to stop me?" he said with great anger. "When I first got your invitation I turned it down because I didn't realize who you were, but when I realized it was you who raised objections at the subcommittee meeting, I just had to tell you face-to-face that decades of my life will be wasted if I can't be the first to use gene therapy on humans."

I was flabbergasted! How could my objection to taking children off enzyme replacement therapy be seen as a threat to Dr. Anderson's career? It simply meant a three month delay so he could redo his paperwork (protocol design, informed consent documents, etc.) and go back to the subcommittee for our final approval.

"Dr. Anderson," I said, "I don't want you to fail. In fact, no one on earth wants you to succeed more than I do because most rare diseases are genetic, and we have been counting on gene therapy technology for the cures we expect. Replacing healthy genes for diseases like cystic fibrosis, hemophilia, muscular dystrophy, etc., have put us closer than we ever imagined to eradicating these diseases. But that does not mean that you should take a child off of a medicine that is keeping them alive. Just add your gene therapy treatments to their usual medical care and then slowly withdraw the PEG-ADA when the gene therapy is working. Any bioethicist would tell you the same thing."

Dr. Anderson calmed a bit, but he then decided to attack PEG-ADA. He told me every reason it was not a good medicine. "It doesn't work," he insisted. "Well, if that's true," I answered, "you will have no trouble withdrawing it after the gene therapy begins to work. It's a win-win for you." I didn't want to remind him that the FDA would not have approved the enzyme therapy unless it was proven to be "effective," but those words would have prolonged Dr. Anderson's anger.

After a while Dr. Anderson calmed down enough to understand that his audience was eagerly awaiting his speech. I explained the composition of the audience he was going to talk to and he became enthusiastic that he would have exposure to a target audience with many genetic diseases. "They are all counting on gene therapy," I emphasized, "because it won't simply be a treatment. It will be a cure, and that's exactly why these support groups exist. They each want to cure their disease so their support group can go out of business," I said with all sincerity.

Dr. Anderson's speech that day to an audience of support group leaders and patients with rare diseases went very well. The audience was extremely grateful they could learn about the status of a cutting-edge medical technology, that knowledge was food for their newsletter stories. The public was becoming more and more excited about gene therapy, part of the reason was our sub-committee meetings, which were open to the public. Reporters attended those meetings and wrote articles that were published throughout the nation, and even the world, giving hope to millions of sick people. Eventually the NIH created an "Office of Biotechnology Activities" which collected the voluminous paperwork coming from scientists, universities and biotech companies, so the public was able to read gene therapy documents on the Internet.

But French Anderson was right to assume he would not be the first person to administer a gene therapy treatment to a patient. Another NIH doctor, a cancer researcher, received permission for a cancer experiment shortly before Dr. Anderson received permission for his SCID-ADA experiment, so Dr. Anderson's test was the second human gene therapy experiment in the United States. Nevertheless, Anderson's status as "the father of gene therapy" was not challenged in the press. His experiment on SCID-ADA was limited to three children, but he could enlarge the clinical trial after he saw progress.

*

The work of the entire RAC committee now focused almost exclusively on human gene therapy. At almost all RAC meetings at NIH, French Anderson sat in the audience, listening to presentations by other scientists who were launching their gene therapy careers and taking notes. He rarely spoke, but when comments from the audience were allowed, he sometimes asked questions.

Every time I saw Dr. Anderson I asked him if he withdrew the PEG-ADA from the children yet. But the answer was always "no." Sometimes he gave me reasons, but after a while he provided no more reasons. But every time Dr. Anderson was interviewed by reporters he would talk about how well the three children were doing. They were actually going to public schools, which they could not do previously because they would have contracted infections from other children that may have killed them. Now, Dr. Anderson told reporters, the three children were getting normal childhood infections and recovering from them, so the gene therapy was working, he declared. Sometimes he would tell a reporter that the gene therapy had "cured" at least one of the children. This raised enormous excitement in the hereditary disease community because support group leaders were certain that their disease would be cured in the foreseeable future. But no evidence of a "cure" was given to the RAC, so I withheld my enthusiasm.

A year or two after I joined the RAC, Dr. Anderson announced that he would be leaving the NIH. He had been at NIH for several decades, so the news was shocking. At the first opportunity I talked to him at length about his plans. "Why are you really leaving the NIH?"I asked him. He responded that his wife, who was also a doctor, had sacrificed her career because she was unable to take a job outside of the Maryland area for many years. Now she was offered a job as a department head in a California hospital, and he didn't want to stand in her way. "She sacrificed so much for me and my career," he said, "It's time that I sacrifice for her." I thought this man deserves an award from the National Organization for Women. How many men would do that for their wife?

Then I asked him to please tell me why he never withdrew the PEG-ADA from the three children in his experiment. He told me it was true that they were recovering from minor childhood infections, but the ultimate test of an immune system is to measure the response of a person to vaccinations. They expect, and they can measure, the antibodies arising in the blood of children who have received a vaccine, but the three SCID-ADA children in his experiment had not manufactured enough antibodies to protect them from some of the most serious diseases. So he kept them on both the PEG-ADA enzyme, the gene therapy and together the drug and the gene therapy were keeping them healthy.

As a member of the RAC it would have been improper for me to tell anyone about this revelation, so I could not warn rare disease support groups to dampen their enthusiasm for gene therapy curing their disease. I congratulated myself for insisting that Dr. Anderson must keep the children on the ADA enzyme. If he had withdrawn them from Adagen, there is no telling what might have happened when the gene therapy failed.

*

W. French Anderson, M.D., was so famous I knew someone or some institution would snap him up in a jiffy knowing he would move to California. Soon he announced that he would be going to the University of Southern California (USC) where they would create a gene therapy laboratory for him so he could continue his research work. He was also on the Board of Directors of a gene therapy company that planned to commercialize the new technology, he also served as an editor of a gene therapy journal. He was not going to sit around wondering what to do next!

Then in 2006 earth shattering news slipped out in California, once the news spread across the country it became even more bizarre. Dr. French Anderson, the world renowned scientist, was a trained Judo master and for decades he had volunteered to teach Judo to children. He gave them Judo lessons in his home studio when he lived in Maryland and continued when he moved to California.

In 2006, W. French Anderson was convicted of sexual abuse of a minor, and in 2007 he was sentenced to 14 years in prison. The victim was the daughter of an employee who worked in Anderson's laboratory at USC, and she was getting Judo lessons from him. When the accusations surfaced in California some Maryland reporters claimed that they interviewed other people who took judo lessons from Anderson in Maryland, they told similar stories. Anderson insisted the accusations were false and the charges were rooted in professional jealousy from the victim's mother.

Anderson's experiments with gene therapy were finished. But his wife has never given up on him and still believes the accusations are false. She has tried mightily to get Anderson released, either on parole or for a new trial. As of 2013 nothing succeeded and Anderson was still in jail. I find the whole situation so bizarre that I have no opinion about his guilt or innocence. The only fault I ever saw in him was a huge ego. But many academic researchers suffer from the same malady. As one researcher told me long ago, "We're not in this business to become millionaires. We're in it because we want to win the Nobel Prize." Yes I can understand that, like Louis Pasteur they want their name to live after them for many centuries because they cured or eradicated a disease.

French Anderson, this brilliant man, with so much to offer humanity, lost everything. The technology that he invented has sputtered and struggled in recent years, one must wonder what might have happened if he had been able to continue his scientific career. But by this time I had seen so much deliberate misleading information virtually shoveled to the popular press by companies trying to inflate their stock price, claiming that gene therapy was going to cure everything even though it had not yet alleviated anything. But members of the committee were not permitted to tell the public that it was all a ruse. So I crossed my fingers and hoped that somehow gene therapy would work on something, because I could not bear to think that the technology could possibly be a failure.

*

Although Dr. Anderson may have been the best known physician trying to bring gene therapy to fruition, other physicians saw the potential. And for many, speed was paramount, while those of us on the RAC urged caution. In one memorable case a doctor wanted to give gene therapy to a child with muscular dystrophy and was racing the clock to announce it on or before the annual muscular dystrophy telethon. The experiment would have injected the vector into a child's toe to see if the gene could restore the muscles in his toe. Nevertheless, standing before the RAC committee the researcher made it sound as if he would cure this child, any delay from the RAC would threaten the child's life. That was absurd, but the press ate up the myth which was purely public relations.

The committee was not going to allow the scientist to abbreviate our discussion, or overlook important data from animal studies, so we took our time going over the details. In the end we decided the experiment wasn't going to prove anything, but it was unlikely that it would cause harm since only one toe would be affected. So we voted yes, the experiment can go forward. The scientist, still standing near the microphone in the RAC meeting room at NIH, dramatically pulled his cell phone out of his pocket, pressed a button and shouted, "It's a go" into the phone. In other words, a team was standing by the patient's bed somewhere in the mid-west, so they could start the experiment immediately with a film crew by their side.

*

Even though gene therapy researchers were required to send us follow-up reports telling us how their patients were doing, they neglected and in some cases refused to give us the reports. I never did learn how well the child's muscular dystrophy toe fared after the experiment, but I assume it failed because the next year there was another telethon begging for more research money.

However, the RAC finally decided that we absolutely had to have the follow-up reports to see whether clinical trial participants benefitted of were harmed by the experiments. Eventually the scientists who performed gene therapy were forced to provide progress reports to the committee, but they wanted the reports to stay confidential. I guessed they were afraid that Wall Street money would dry up if investors realized that gene therapy was not working. The reports showed that most of the experiments were on different forms of cancer, and after the gene therapy infusion patients with cancer continued to die from progression of their disease. Patients with hereditary conditions continued to have those diseases.

When we received the reports we had no choice but to keep the reports quiet while gene therapy companies continued to tell Wall Street that they were saving lives, investors were told that gene therapy was almost ready for commercialization.....in two or three years.

Then Jesse Gelsinger died and everything changed.

Jesse had a urea cycle disorder, one of the very rare orphan diseases that Saul Brusilow's medicine treated. As a child he took his medicine and stayed on a strict diet, but when he became a teenager it was more important to hang out with his friends, skip his medicine and eat the things that his friends ate and drank. Jesse's father was overwrought with worry because Jesse would go into a coma and need intensive care in a hospital until the ammonia in his blood could be reduced. Odds that he would survive such a coma were not very good.

When he was about 18 years old Jesse came to his senses. He took his medicine, he stayed on his diet and his life turned around. Jesse's father, Paul Gelsinger, was a concerned father who tried mightily to show his son the path to a good life, and he succeeded. Then when Jesse was 19 he was contacted by Dr. James Wilson of the University of Pennsylvania, who was one of the gene therapy whiz-kids who was admired and respected by his fellow gene therapy scientists. I remember, for example, when the RAC reviewed one of Dr. Wilson's protocol's for an upcoming clinical trial, one of the reviewers described the experiment as "elegant", an unusual term from one scientist to another.

Dr. Wilson contacted Jesse because he wanted to do a small clinical trial on the type of urea cycle disorder that Jesse had, ornithine transcarbamylase deficiency. Although the disorder is an X-linked genetic disease, Jesse's form seems to have resulted from a spontaneous genetic mutation within the womb and was not inherited. Therefore, some of Jesse's cells were normal and could manufacture some of the enzyme that he needed, but not all that he needed. Wilson reasoned that trying the gene therapy on someone who is not severely affected will lead the way to treating more severely affected children in the future.

Dr. Wilson was honest and told Jesse it was unlikely that the experiment would help him, but he hoped whatever was learned from the experiment would help children born with the disease in the future. That did it for Jesse! He told his father he would participate in the experiment because he "wanted to help the babies" who would have his disease in the future.

So Jesse, whose disease was under control most of the time with diet and medicine, flew from Arizona to Pennsylvania to participate in Dr. Wilson's experiment. Patients who participate in clinical trials cannot benefit financially from their participation, but Jesse's travel and accommodation costs were covered by the University so there were no costs for Jesse.

A few days later Paul Gelsinger received a phone call from Dr. Wilson's office. Something had gone wrong, Jesse had an extreme reaction to the gene therapy. He was in intensive care and in a coma. Paul flew to Philadelphia immediately. Jesse died on Sept. 17, 1999, only four days after he was injected with Dr. Wilson's gene therapy.

The cause of death was from a massive immune system response that shut down Jesse's vital organs. The FDA issued a report finding Dr. Wilson and some of his co-workers at fault. They found that Jesse Gelsinger was a substitute for another volunteer who had dropped out. But previous to the procedure Jesse's blood was tested and he had high ammonia levels, so he should have been excluded from the trial. Additionally, the University had not reported to the FDA that two previous patients in the trial had experienced serious side effects from the gene therapy. Nor had they disclosed in the informed consent document that monkeys had died from an infusion of the gene therapy before the human trial began.

The RAC was absolutely shaken when we heard about Jesse's death. Was there anything we could have done to prevent the tragedy? We discovered that Dr. Wilson or someone else at the University had changed the protocol and not come back to the RAC for approval of the changes. Additionally, RAC scientists had warned that the infusion should not take place in or near the liver; the protocol we approved would have infused the mixture into the bloodstream through a distant vein, but it had indeed been infused in the main vessel feeding Jesse's liver. The RAC was never informed of this change. Also, the informed consent document was not the document that the RAC approved, it did not reveal that both Dr. Wilson and the University of Pennsylvania had a financial stake in the company that was developing the treatment for commercialization, which was unknown to the Gelsinger family.

The worst bioethical violations came together in Dr. Wilson's trial, it resulted in the death of a promising young man who just wanted to help the next generation of children with his disease. The compulsion of private companies to label anything as a "trade secret" that they wanted to keep secret, had overstepped the boundaries of common sense. Patients who volunteered their bodies for the clinical trial had a right to know, Dr. Wilson was obligated to tell them, about the deaths of animals in pre-clinical gene therapy trials and the severe reactions of the two human patients who received the gene therapy infusions before Jesse.

There were enough mistakes made in this experiment to result in the University of Pennsylvania agreeing to an out-of-court settlement with the Gelsinger family. Dr. Wilson continued to work in his gene therapy lab, but he was not allowed by the FDA to lead human trials for five years. But the biggest losers in this scenario were other scientists in the gene therapy field because the RAC became much stricter about its duties and responsibilities. Any change of protocol, however minor, had to come back to the RAC for approval.

As Mark Twain once wrote, "There is something fascinating about science. One gets such wholesale returns of conjecture out of such a trifling investment of fact." Yes indeed, we can imagine all the things gene therapy is capable of doing, all the diseases it will cure and imagine what it could do for future generations! But, what has it done so far? And what evidence do we have that it will live up to its promise in the future?

*

A few years before I retired wonderful news came out of France that gene therapy by French doctors on 10 children with SCID-X1, a different subtype from SCID-ADA, were CURED (that magic word again). However, about two years later one of those children came down with a form of leukemia. Investigators found that when the viral vectors were infused into a human there was no way to direct them where they should fall, and apparently some vectors dropped the good gene on an "oncogene." Oncogenes control cell growth and when they are damaged or mutated they can cause cancer. A few years later five of the 10 children had come down with leukemia, and more may experience the same adverse event over time.

Meanwhile, biotechnology companies have tamped down their language about gene therapy being the new magic medicine of modern times. Gene therapy has been replaced by new magic words: "stem cells." How can gene therapy companies raise money from investors with all the bad news about gene therapy lingering in the press? Investors began to wonder if the fledgling therapy was safe enough and what requirements the FDA would impose before approving a gene therapy. When I served on the RAC there were dozens of companies asking for permission to start new clinical trials, but now there are apparently very few. Jesse's death enabled some of the worst problems of the field to reach the light of day. Neither patients nor investors want to be lied to, they certainly don't want to think that money played any role in influencing medical decisions. The data about the fate of clinical trial participants who underwent gene therapy could no longer be hidden after Jesse's death. Hardly any participants who entered gene therapy trials with a fatal disease are still alive.

Despite the setbacks and problems, I always hoped that someday scientists would figure out how to get gene therapy to work because despite everything it still holds the possibility of a cure, not an ongoing treatment, for many devastating diseases.

*

As I mentioned earlier, in November, 2012 the European Union approved the very first gene therapy product to get on the European market. Scientists had after decades of promises and research and false starts finally delivered! Glybera is manufactured by a Dutch firm called uniQure. It is a treatment for lipoprotein lipase deficiency (LLD), which affects one to two people per million. That means with a population of 300 million Americans, only 300 to 600 cases are in the United States.

However, the manufacturer announced it will charge $1,200,000 for the therapy. Since European countries operate national medical systems, which means their governments pay for medical services and medicines, that cost could put the success of the treatment in jeopardy. We will have to wait and see if any national health agency in Europe is willing to pay that price. And ultimately we will greatly anticipate that the children who receive the gene therapy in Europe will not relapse and will not get cancer from the therapy itself in future years.

LLD is a genetic disease characterized by an inability to break down fats, causing life threatening conditions such as pancreatitis, diabetes and clogged arteries. The vector for Glybera is an adeno-associated virus implanted with a normal lipoprotein lipase gene that makes the needed enzyme in muscle cells. There is no other treatment available for this disease, although some individuals can be successfully treated by dietary restriction of fats.

*

During President Clinton's closing days in office I was appointed to the Dept. of Health and Human Services (DHHS) Research Protections Advisory Committee (2000-2002). This was the first chance we had to review and rewrite the Human Research Protections for people who volunteer for scientific research and clinical trials. I kept Doris Zallen's re-write of the research protections for gene therapy volunteers and I was determined to incorporate some of her ideas inserted into the new document. We worked hard on that re-write; we studied the current rules and where they failed to protect patients, we were proud of what we did. Then a few days before our last meeting, where we would finalize the draft that we agreed upon, each member of the committee received a phone call from Washington. The last meeting was cancelled and the National Human Research Protections Advisory Committee was dissolved. The new President, George W. Bush, would name a new committee in coming weeks.

President Bush had his own agenda, so he would appoint a new committee that would agree with his agenda. Mainly he wanted to make sure that fetal stem cells would not be used for research. To him a fetus was a living baby, even if it was only four or eight cells big. So our rewrite of human research protections went down the drain and it was never published or implemented.

I cannot help wondering, however, if President Clinton's decision to improve human protections in research, known in the government as "The Common Rule," was spurred by the Jesse Gelsinger disaster. Unfortunately, we will never know. And I continue to be haunted by those horrible words that I heard so many years ago, "Let someone else's child be the guinea pig."

At this point in history no one deserves to be a human guinea pig. That is why human research protections need to be updated and refined.

Chapter 14

Reflections

"When an old person dies, a library burns to the ground."

African proverb

Now that I'm retired, the thing that most people ask me first is what do I think about the accomplishments of the Orphan Drug Act? Has it been as successful as I thought it would be? Have I been disappointed in any aspect of the law?

The successes of the law are numerous. The medical advances in the last 30 years have been remarkable and some of them are a direct result of the ODA. Tremendously promising therapies are being studied today; many of which rely on the provisions of the ODA.

Many treatments for children and adults with rare diseases are used every single day; treatments that would never have existed without the ODA. It is hard to deny the many successes of the law. However, when I'm asked about the ODA and its impact, I prefer to answer with the adage:

"Be careful what you wish for. You just might get it."

*

In 1983 when, against all odds, President Reagan signed the Orphan Drug Act into law, we knew about approximately 15 or 20 orphan drugs that needed commercial sponsors. Therefore, I expected a few companies to step up and adopt them, and put them on the road to FDA approval immediately. So in the first few years I was disappointed that it was taking so long to get the first orphan drugs on the market.

I had to learn about the FDA's drug approval process, and where the barriers were. Each drug had to go through a specific review committee, with scientists and physicians from specific areas of medicine. A drug for a gastrointestinal disease, for example, would not be reviewed by the committee that specializes in eye diseases or neurological diseases. However, even if a drug is routed through the proper review committee, the committee members may know little or nothing about the rare disease that the orphan drug is aimed at. There was no provision for the FDA to consult with outside experts who were knowledgeable about specific rare diseases.

It took time for the advantages of the law to sink into the brains of pharmaceutical CEOs. To have a guaranteed 7 year period without competition was a major bonus that was not immediately obvious to them. And the tax credits for the cost of clinical research could only be used by profitable companies. Most of the small biotechnology companies were not yet profitable. Ironically, in 2013, 30 years after the passage of the ODA, some of the companies that fought against the tax credits are now fighting to preserve the credits because they can now be carried forward or back and used in a year that the company is profitable.

Most new drugs qualify for a 20 year patent, but most companies file their patent application for a new drug extremely early, before it emerges from a laboratory to be tested on humans. By the time they complete their research and receive FDA approval to market the drug, they often have 5 to 7 years left on their patent. But another company could make slight changes to the molecule and obtain FDA approval to market a closely related drug because even though it was "similar," it would be a "New Molecular Entity" (NME). That's why when a new blockbuster drug like Viagra comes to market, other companies shave off a molecule here and add a molecule there, and voila…a new molecular entity is born to compete with the original blockbuster drug.

However, orphan drug "exclusivity" is different from a "patent." If you are awarded orphan drug exclusivity, the FDA is prohibited from approving another similar drug for the same disease, for seven years. The manufacturer of the similar drug would have to prove that it is "clinically superior" to the original drug, therefore it is "different" in order to get on the market before the seventh year expires. Additionally, the clock starts ticking on a patent from the day when you file the patent application, but the clock on orphan drug exclusivity starts on the day that the FDA approves the drug for sale in the United States.

During the 1980s each new orphan drug that reached the market was greeted with fanfare, but in the 1990s small and medium sized drug and biotechnology companies finally understood the benefits of the law. For the most part it was not the large multi-national pharmaceutical companies that developed the most new orphan drugs. A new industry of small and medium sized companies evolved to adopt the majority of drugs for small populations of people.

Small and medium sized drug and biotechnology companies learned during the 1990s that the words "orphan drug" could get the attention of Wall Street and venture capitalists. The company would apply to the FDA for an orphan drug designation, and months later when the FDA issued the designation, the company would send out press releases to the financial community, hoping that investors would find the company attractive.

Keep in mind that to get an orphan drug designation you do not have to prove anything to the FDA except that the target population for the drug is under 200,000 people in the United States, and you must explain the scientific rationale that makes your company believe the drug will work on that orphan disease. To obtain an orphan drug designation you do not have to show that the drug actually works on the targeted disease, nor that it is safe for human use. That information can only come after clinical trials prove that a drug is safe and effective. However, some drugs never get out of the starting gate because they simply don't work, and other drugs may turn out to be too toxic for human use.

By 2013 there were approximately 450 approved orphan drugs on the U.S. market, approximately 3,000 designated orphan drugs, either in various stages of development, or abandoned because they were unsafe or ineffective.

One might say the rare disease patient community got what it wished for, except for the cost. No one imagined the heights to which orphan drug prices could surge.

*

One thing I learned in my years at NORD is that medical science often moves at a glacial pace. Despite the incentives granted by the ODA, the science – the research – still has to be conducted and there is no guarantee that the treatment will benefit the patients you intended it for.

Today, there are many intriguing potential therapies under investigation. Pig viruses, pancreas tissue transplants, human subject protections in research, prions and stem cells, RNAi-based gene therapy, the use of the measles vaccine to fight cancer; all at the cutting edge of science, all representing challenging puzzles that can either frighten patients or inspire them with boundless hope.

These promising therapies also serve to remind us just how much farther we have to go. If scientists could figure out the cause of Kuru and prevent it from wiping out an indigenous tribe, why can't they figure out the cause of Alzheimer's disease? And could the prions that cause Kuru also be causing Alzheimer's disease, Lou Gehrig's disease (ALS), or any of the mysterious neurological conditions that have no obvious cause or cure?

One of the major barriers to advancements in medical science is, and perhaps always will be, funding. How can we ensure that the Jonas Salks of the next generation will stay in medical research? Every year they have to struggle to win challenging competitions for research grants while Congress cuts back on research appropriations. It's not an easy way to make a living, especially because their former colleagues who left research and went into private practice or health related businesses are living in big houses, driving expensive cars and collecting the huge bonuses that educated business professionals expect in the American private sector.

Today the latest technologies always have the most promising futures, because we still don't know what their futures may hold. Right now it's "stem cells," but will the future of stem cells live up to their promise of future treatments and cures, or will another hopeful technology grab center stage until it again disappoints to ultimately wither and die?

Embryonic stem cells can be coaxed into becoming just about any kind of cell that scientists want, so it should be possible to coax stem cells into becoming insulin factories, or to grow liver or kidney cells, etc. For the first ten years of stem cell excitement they were embroiled in the Bush-era anti-abortion debate, so little progress was made. When Obama was elected he lifted the restrictions so fetal stem cells could be used, but we still don't know whether the cells will live up to their initial promise. Medical research takes years and years of grueling work in the laboratory and the clinic. And sometimes it just doesn't pan out.

I do know one thing for certain. When I retired there were many new patient advocates out there willing to take my place, waiting to wave the flag and inspire people to fight for the medically disenfranchised. Each of them has fought for their own children, their own spouse or parent and they have risen above their individual sphere of concern to care about others. They are capable. They can do it. Many people must walk together before a new road comes into existence.

*

Once an orphan drug is "designated" by the FDA, the company has to design a plan for clinical trials. First they have to show the FDA pre-clinical tests that indicate the compound seems safe enough to be tested in humans. Obviously, no one really knows if it is safe until humans actually use it. How big should the clinical trials be? Where will they be conducted? How long will the testing go on? The FDA prefers large clinical trials, but some rare diseases are so rare the FDA cannot require a trial on 1,000 patients if there are only 100 patients with the diagnosis in the United States.

Much of this is guess work because no company can predict where they will find enough patients and whether the patients will be willing to participate in human tests. Since people with rare diseases are not clustered around big cities, it can take time to find enough of them, and since some will live far away from testing centers, the company may have to make pre-paid travel arrangements for the patient and a care-giver to travel to the testing facility. Pharmaceutical and biotechnology companies working on a treatment for a specific rare disease must identify the experts and thought leaders for that disease, because those experts will likely know where the patients are.

Thus clinical trials of an orphan drug can take more time than anticipated, especially if it takes too much time to find the patients. But none of that time is subtracted from the seven years of exclusivity when the drug is approved for marketing, whereas these types of delays tend to eat away at drug patents.

*

Are there disappointments? The main attraction of the ODA is the provision for 7 years of exclusivity, 7 years without competition. Some companies have used the absence of competition to wring out every last cent that a patient will pay for their medicine. Ultimately, it is the extraordinarily high prices for orphan drugs that threaten its future.

In the United States companies are free to charge any amount that they want for a drug, some have been shamelessly greedy. We have long known that companies will adopt and manufacture a drug that makes money for them, that is the basis of the Orphan Drug Act. Provisions of the law assume that a company will not lose money if they develop a drug for a rare disease, and indeed they will very likely make a profit on their orphan drug. We expected high prices, but we never imagined that some companies would set the price of their drug higher than the price of a new house. For chronic diseases this means purchasing their orphan drug every year is like buying a new house every year…$200,000 to $500,000 every year, for the rest of your life! Why do companies price an orphan drug so high? Because other companies have done this before them,and insurers have paid the price if the disease is very rare and life-threatening.

On the other hand one has to understand how the prices for all new drugs are set. It rarely has anything to do with the cost of developing the drug.

If you are developing a drug for high blood pressure or high cholesterol, you expect that millions of people will be taking your drug. So if you design the price around the amount it cost you to develop the drug, knowing millions of people will take your drug every day, you can tack on a few cents to every pill for your profit **as long as your price is competitive with the prices of other blood pressure or cholesterol pills**. Since you will sell millions of pills to millions of patients every day for the remaining patent life of your drug, you can calculate how much money the sales of that drug will bring to your company while the patent is in effect. If your estimates are not accurate, you can raise the price of your drug as time goes on.

However, if you are selling the drug to a small population of people with a rare disease, the cost of a daily dose will be much higher than a blood pressure or cholesterol pill because the manufacturer has to earn back his investment and make a profit, while few customers are buying the drug. Naturally, manufacturers will tack on a higher profit on every pill or injection, because fewer people will buy the drug. The cost of the profit cannot be spread around to millions of people when you manufacture an orphan drug.

Yes, orphan drugs are more expensive than ordinary drugs, but they have to be because they have fewer "customers" who will buy the drug. But when a company tells Wall Street that sales of its orphan drug in North America to only 1,000 patients will generate over $1 billion annually, something is wrong. How much profit is too much? Why isn't a company satisfied with a quarter-billion dollars in sales annually? A half-billion?

Of course this is occurring only because the United States does not control the pricing of drugs. All other western industrialized countries do control drug prices, but some of the European countries have chosen to get around this orphan drug pricing problem by simply not paying for drugs that they deem too expensive. The two step process of drug approval in Europe is: 1) marketing approval for the EU market based on scientific evidence of safety and effectiveness, and 2) qualifying for payment by the reimbursement authority in each country. Expensive orphan drugs sometimes do not qualify for reimbursement in certain European countries.

Sometimes in the American reimbursement system which is based on the private sector, our health insurance company may refuse to pay for an expensive drug, our only option may be through the courts. Sometimes a pharmaceutical company may negotiate a lower price with a government health system (e.g., the Veterans' Administration or Medicaid), or a health insurance company, but these agreements often remain confidential so that other customers don't know how much the price has been discounted to each buyer. Patients without health insurance are generally charged the standard retail price without any discounts, unless the pharmaceutical company has a Patient Assistance Program.

*

If we take the 7 years of exclusivity out of the ODA, the law would fail to promote the development of treatments for rare diseases. If you make it too difficult for manufacturers to recoup the cost of developing the drug AND to make a profit, the industry would turn its back on orphan drugs. This is why I cringe when I hear a politician declare he wants to change the ODA because too many greedy companies are pricing their drugs beyond common sense. The accusations may be correct, but the solution is wrong.

On the other hand pharmaceutical companies have not provided any solutions at all. Some of them inherently know where the price cut-off should be, before the price attracts too much attention. But other companies don't care that they are putting the ODA in jeopardy by charging an awesome amount for a year of therapy. They simply want to go on doing what they've been doing for the past 30 years, hoping that politicians have bigger fish to fry.

I worry that someday the ODA will be in jeopardy. If it's not the pricing issue, it will be one of the many companies who want to change the law so it favors one or more of their products. When a new lobbying campaign to change the ODA begins, it is difficult to find out who is funding it and why. But eventually we find out because the legislation they are pushing has a tell-tale sign of self-interest. I cannot protect the law forever, I cringe when I think what could happen when self-involved manufacturers hit the immoveable force of Congress. The patients will be the losers if the ODA is changed.

During the years that I was President and CEO of NORD I was reminded daily that the purpose of our work was to aid patients and families with rare diseases. Everybody who worked at NORD communicated every day with desperate people who had nowhere else to turn for help, it gave us all a purpose far beyond money and perks that the average private sector worker cares about. If you could save a family from falling into bankruptcy by providing him or her with free drugs for up to a year, you went home feeling good. If you could link a grieving family with a genetic clinic that could test other family members for a disease causing gene, it felt good. And if you could link a disease researcher with enough patients so he or she could finish a clinical trial on a new treatment, you knew that every day you were making miracles that mattered in people's lives. Nevertheless, no matter how hard I tried I could never make a miracle for Eric Lopez who had epidermolysis bullosa (EB).

EB is a group of rare connective tissue diseases in which the skin is extremely fragile and will blister and tear from minor friction or trauma, especially on the hands and feet. In some cases EB can be mild, but in many cases especially those that are inherited through recessive genes, it can be severe and extremely painful and debilitating. Skin blistering can become infected and blistering can also occur internally affecting the esophagus, upper airways, stomach, urinary tract and intestines.

Eric's mother, Arlene Pessar, was a Jewish woman from Brooklyn who married a man who was from Puerto Rico. Of course this set the stage for another West Side Story saga, with both families disapproving of their child marrying out of their culture. Arlene became pregnant and her son Eric was born with much of his skin missing. He had to be treated like a burn victim by wrapping the raw areas of his body with bandages and gauze. Eric was quickly diagnosed with the recessive genetic form of epidermolysis bullosa because a doctor at the maternity hospital had seen the disease symptoms before.

EB can be inherited from one parent in an autosomal dominant manner or from both parents in an autosomal recessive manner. If a genetic disease is inherited from dominant genes, only one parent who has the faulty gene is necessary to pass the disease on to their children. But when a disease is inherited through recessive genes both parents must contribute the faulty gene to the affected child. Many familiar but rare diseases are passed on through this manner such as cystic fibrosis (approximately 30,000 cases in the United States). Eric had a severe form of EB that was inherited in an autosomal recessive manner.

Neither Arlene nor her husband was aware that the EB gene ran in their families – neither of them had any skin problems and none of their relatives had developed EB. People with a recessive disease gene can go several generations without the disease appearing, especially if their spouse does not have the defective gene. But even if both parents do have the recessive gene, there is a 25 percent chance for each individual pregnancy that the child will inherit both faulty genes from both parents, thus will have the disease. There is approximately a 50 percent chance that a child will inherit only one of the faulty genes from one parent. These children are carriers for the disorder and usually will never develop any symptoms (although in some specific instances they can develop very mild expressions of a disorder). In these families there is also a 25 percent chance that a child will not inherit either of the faulty genes and will be healthy.

It is almost a Las Vegas style craps shoot, some families may get no sign of the disease while in other families most or all of their children may get the disease when they inherit two of the faulty genes; one from each parent. There is no way to predict how much of a family will be affected because doctors only know the odds.

Eric Lopez inherited the faulty EB gene from his mother and his father. The father looked at the child and walked out, leaving Arlene to raise him herself. One doctor in the hospital told her Eric's life would be filled with pain and suffering and advised her to let him die quickly from infection. She could not accept that advice and was determined that Eric would live.

Arlene moved back to her family in Brooklyn. She realized the only way Eric would survive would be if she could learn as much as possible about the disease. Since there was no medicine to treat the disorder she felt the key would be good nursing care. Wrapping and re-wrapping the bandages, making sure that food was not hot enough to cause blisters in Eric's esophagus, avoiding trauma and moving him in a wheelchair. So Arlene went to nursing school and became a nurse.

Eventually Arlene learned about a British organization known as DEBRA (Dystrophic Epidermolysis Bullosa Research Association). She saw DEBRA as the answer to many of Eric's problems and hers, so she created an American DEBRA in New York. Knowing she could never raise enough money to make a dent in the need for EB research, she decided she would lobby Congress for EB research funding. Eric saw this as a worthy cause so he often accompanied Arlene to Washington when she made her appeals for EB funding at the National Institutes of Health (NIH). One sight of Eric in his wheelchair, with his sparse hair and bandaged limbs, broke the hearts of powerful elected officials and thus language was put into NIH funding legislation to bring attention to the need for EB research. However, few dermatologists opt to do research, it was a struggle to get them interested enough in EB to apply for NIH research funding.

I first met Eric and Arlene at a rare disease conference at the University of Michigan. I gave a carefully prepared speech that I thought was well received, but when there was a break in the proceedings a young teenage boy rolled up to me in his wheelchair angrily asking why I did not mention the name of his disease in my speech. I was ashamed to answer him, but eventually I had to say, "Eric, I cannot pronounce the name of your disease. And I can't say "EB" because no one will know what I'm talking about.

"Epi-derm-ol-ysis-bullosa," he said. "Repeat after me." I had no choice, so I repeated it again several times, from that time forward I always mentioned epidermolysis bullosa in major speeches, for fear that Eric might find out that I omitted mention of EB.

Eric was brilliant, and since Arlene's special care enabled him to live until he passed the age of 20, he applied to an excellent engineering school, the Brooklyn Polytechnic Institute. The accommodations Eric needed in high school were an accessible building, so he could use his wheelchair and air conditioning in the rooms he occupied because when he sweated he would get more blisters. Eric's hands were covered in huge blisters that looked like mittens. Sometimes he would get surgery to uncover his fingers, but the blisters would grow back. Nevertheless, teenage boys have a strong streak of independence, Eric wished he could be independent of his mother so he needed his fingers to write and eat without help.

Eric started college and was doing quite well with his academics, then things started to fall apart. He dropped out of school and decided to accept that his handicaps greatly limited him. I asked Arlene what had happened. She explained that at lunchtime Eric would leave school and roll his wheelchair to a nearby diner where he would order lunch. He did this every day until one day when the diner's owner came to talk to him. He told Eric he admired him for being independent enough to come to the restaurant every day, but the way Eric looked, wrapped in the bandages and no visible fingers, and was upsetting to other customers. He asked Eric not to come back because he needed other customers to eat at his restaurant every day.

When Arlene told me what happened I was shocked and outraged! What about Eric's civil rights! The diner owner could not tell a black person, or a woman, or a Muslim, etc., not to eat at his restaurant, but he could tell a handicapped person not to come back! I spoke to Eric and told him I would find a lawyer who would fight this outrageous violation of his civil rights. But his voice sounded weak, as if he knew it was time to give up the fight. "I don't want to go where I'm not welcome," he said.

Eric died at the age of 24. I wondered how Arlene would find the strength to carry on, but she did. She went back to nursing for a while, then she got a job at a health insurance company where she talked to patients and advised them when they were having problems. She felt useful to other people who needed her help, but she could not maintain a relationship with DEBRA because it was too difficult for her to think about EB. In the end, it was the blisters on Eric's internal organs that killed him.

The last time I spoke to her was two or three years after the Sept. 11th, 2001 terrorist attack. Arlene worked in one of the towers of the World Trade Center. When the hijacked planes hit the building she knew not to wait and she exited the building immediately. But when she got to the street there was no transportation or any means of getting away quickly. So she followed mobs of people to the shoreline and took a boat without caring where the boat was going. Eventually she ended up in New Jersey, and someone later brought her home to Brooklyn, by car.

What did she learn? This woman who bore a child needing round the clock care; created a charity to provide help and support services to other families with EB; single handedly got government to understand the need for research on EB; traveled the world to get research dermatologists interested in EB. Arlene told me that after Eric died she didn't want to go on living, but on Sept. 11, 2001, "I learned that I wanted to live. I was so scared, I couldn't think of anything else. I just wanted to live."

We all just want to live – even those of us with rare, painful and even debilitating disorders. Unfortunately, in the case of EB and many other serious rare disorders, there remains no cure and no effective therapy. Treatment is aimed at alleviating symptoms and attempting to minimize complications and pain associated with the disorder. But the course of the underlying disease cannot be altered.

So, when questions arise about the ODA and its future, I think about all the amazing people I've met in my career. It's impossible to recount all of their stories – each one poignant and important in its own way. But one person I'll never forget is Eric Lopez. And when I think about the impact of the ODA, I think of him and all the other people with rare diseases who have suffered, struggled and persevered, I know that the ODA has to continue to entice pharmaceutical manufacturers so they will be ready to manufacture the next treatment, the next cure for horrendous diseases such as epidermolysis bullosa.

*

When I retired I spent about 2 years painting, to get creativity out of my system, then another couple of years reading all the books that I never had time to read when I was working. And then I thought

I had better write it all down because the miracle of ordinary people getting a federal law passed is so unbelievable! Before the law was enacted, people with rare diseases were like the victims of Eugenics.....they didn't matter because they were "different." Even today I hear politicians making speeches in favor of "conquering" the "major health threats" of cancer, heart disease and Alzheimer's. What does that statement say to people with rare diseases? Are rare diseases "minor health threats" that don't matter?

Yes we do matter!

That is the message I want to leave to the world. It doesn't matter if you have Creutzfeld-Jakob disease or Alzheimer's disease – they both destroy your brain. And it's important to find out whether pig viruses are dangerous to other species, and do we humans have viruses in our genome? And someone has to protect the patients who participate in biomedical research, but the university's lawyer is not the person to do it.

So now that I'm finished writing it all down, I'll go back to painting, hoping I can recapture the talent I had when my children were small. I do, however, regret that we didn't empty that Korean orphanage of all its children. Every single one of those orphans should have mattered more than the business enterprise of the orphanage manager. At the very least she could have hired enough staff to ensure that every baby would be talked to and turned in its crib each day so it's skull would not be malformed. I cannot go back and change it now, but I will always regret walking away.

As with Aesop's fables I am tempted to provide a moral to this story. I could not solve the problem for my son or for my family without the strength of other families stricken by other rare diseases. It was all of us working together that built an impregnable movement demanding a solution. In the end, with the help of government and a touch of Hollywood, the forces opposing us could not win. But nothing would have been accomplished without dedicated research scientists and the pharmaceutical industry who translated our dreams into reality. I only wish I could personally thank all of the thousands of people who took this journey with me and built the impenetrable wall of strength that the worldwide Orphan Disease movement stands upon today.

After 30 years, finally, orphan drugs are being adopted and made available to people who need them. And finally, due to ObamaCare, Americans have health insurance so medical goods and services are finally available to the American people who need them, even if they have a "pre-existing condition" and even if they have a rare disease.

Abbey Meyers and Rep. Henry Waxman at the 30th anniversary of the Orphan Drug Act. After 30 years the extraordinary accomplishments of the ODA were evident throughout the world.